# SuperWorlds

By Joshua Strickland

Introduction by Erich von Däniken
Illustrations by Gary Tong

Grosset & Dunlap • Publishers • New York

ACKNOWLEDGMENTS

Maps of Northern and Southern skies, endpapers: These maps, amended, are reproduced from *Norton's Star Atlas,* by permission of Gall & Inglis Edinburgh, Scotland.

Chart, pages 14-15 and bottom of page 118: Reproduced with permission of the Council of the Royal Society of Edinburgh from *Proceedings,* 50, 1929/30, p. 196.

Chart, page 54: From *Astronomy,* by William T. Skilling and Robert S. Richardson, Copyright, 1947, by Holt, Rinehart and Winston, Publishers. Reprinted by permission of Holt, Rinehart and Winston, Publishers.

Chart, page 55: From *A Brief Text in Astronomy,* Revised Edition, by William T. Skilling and Robert S. Richardson. Copyright © 1954, 1959 by Holt, Rinehart and Winston, Publishers. Reproduced by permission of Holt, Rinehart and Winston, Publishers.

Interstellar message with interpretations, page 112: Reproduced by permission from *Intelligent Life in the Universe,* by I. S. Shklovskii and Carl Sagan (Holden Day, San Francisco, 1966; Dell Publishing Company, New York, 1967).

Data and chart on pages 18, 115, 116, and top of 118: Reproduced by permission from *Man and the Stars,* by Duncan Lunan, Souvenir Press, London, 1974. Published in the United States under the title *Interstellar Contact,* Henry Regnery Company, Chicago, 1975.

1976 Printing
Library of Congress Catalog Card Number: 74-92

ISBN: 0-448-12568-4 (Paperback Edition)
ISBN: 0-448-13261-3 (Library Edition)


Published simultaneously in Canada.
Printed in the United States of America.

# Introduction

Every human being, even an infant, is equipped with a computer, that is, the brain. Molecular memory units and nerve-shunt elements store and process data transmitted through millions of receptors all over the body. The environment, peopled with parents, friends, priests, and teachers, funnels prefiltered data into human computers through the eyes and ears. The brain registers emotions like joy, pain, desire, love, hatred. Everyone strives for satisfaction of "pleasure." But what is pleasure to one may be displeasure to another.

The educated man's brain is extensively programmed. He knows what he wants to do and why. In this connection, professional success always means "achievement of pleasure." Attack on its personal professional field, the brain registers as "displeasure." Nobody likes to be shamed. Thus we understand why new thoughts, theories, and theses are always rejected.

For decades, Leonardo da Vinci worked secretly on the construction of flying machines. When his drawings were finally published, the reaction was unanimous: machines heavier than air could never lift off the ground.

In a 1924 review of Professor Hermann Oberth's book *Rocket to the Planetary Spaces,* the world-famous periodical *Nature* commented that a space rocket would probably be perfected shortly before the extinction of the human race.

New theories fare badly.

Max Planck, winner of the Nobel Prize in Physics, arrived at the following conclusion on the basis of his own experiences: ". . . as a rule, new scientific truth is not accepted by its opponents acknowledging recognition and declaring themselves convinced. Instead, it wins out because its adversaries pass away and the new generation has been from the start acquainted with the truth."

Despite opposition, therefore, new ideas are introduced. Flying machines, a figment of the imagination in the eighteenth century, travel all over the world today. Vehicles capable of flight into space have been built, and even now the American spacecraft Pioneer 10 voyages to the unknown. *Superworlds* examines many ideas that once belonged to the realm of fantasy. Intelligent life on other planets in other galaxies? Absurd! Absurd? Here the author gives some of the reasons why many scientists believe there may be other life-bearing planets, some inhabited by intelligent, technological civilizations that may be even more advanced than our own.

Where shall we look for these civilizations? What are the conditions that favor life? How long does it take for a technological society to develop? Is a probe from outer space trying to signal us? How can we interpret these signals? And how can we transmit signals of our own? Can we reach other galaxies? What obstacles might we encounter? Would we learn after extensive research that only computerized spacecraft can endure the hardships of space travel? Or is it possible that human beings can embark on a voyage into space? How long would it take? What strange phenomena would space travelers face? Could they return? What would they return to?

These questions are not new. The stars and what we might find in space have intrigued mankind from the earliest times. Nor can we pretend that there are definitive answers. Based on what is known, however, we can consider the awesome possibilities. These possibilities are examined thoroughly and lucidly in this thought-provoking book that may take you on your first journey to the stars.

Erich von Däniken
Zurich, 1975

# Contents

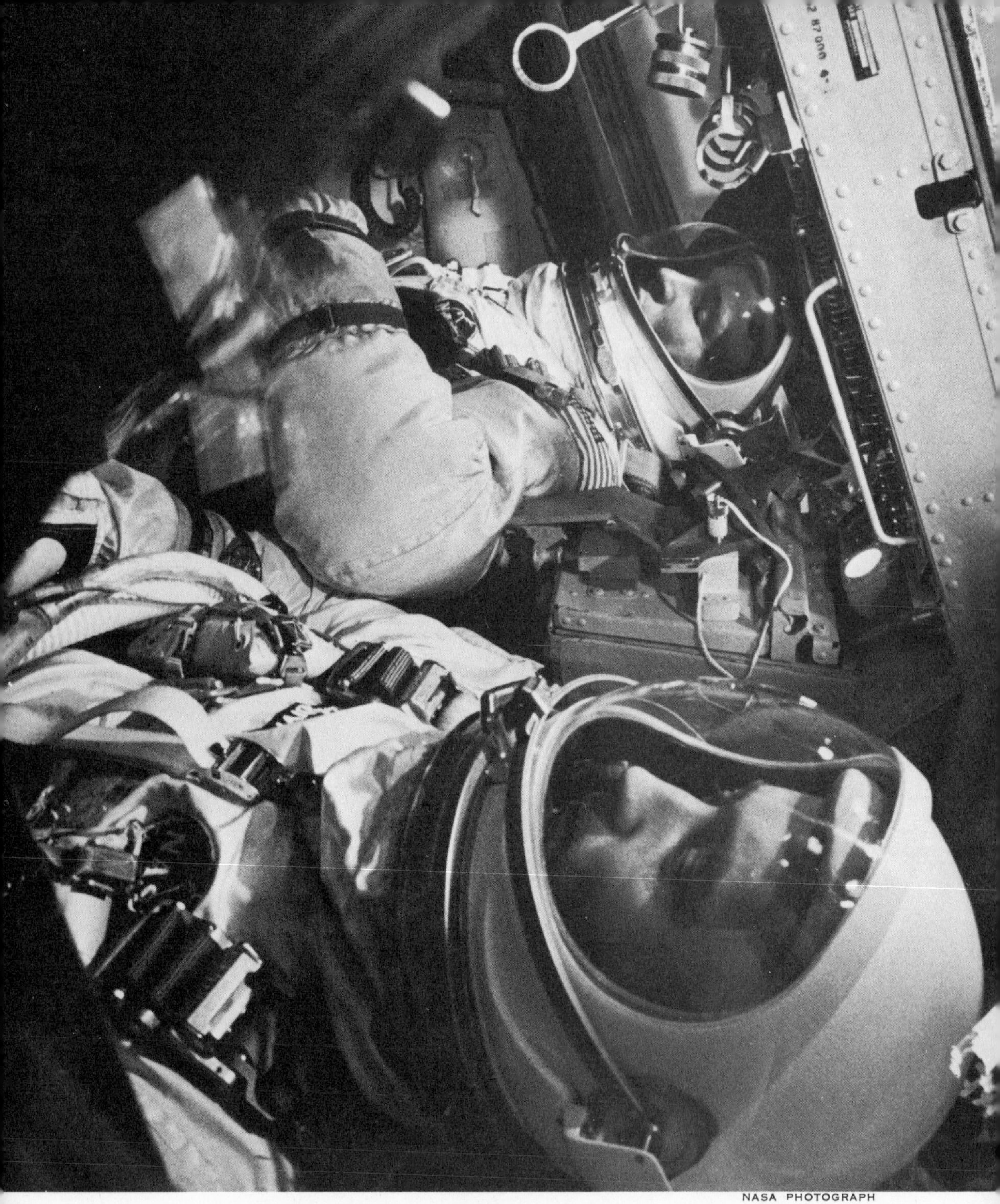

NASA PHOTOGRAPH

Astronaut James McDivitt may have been the first Earthling to see something made by a SuperWorld. It was in orbit over the Pacific.

# 1: Visitors From Outer Space

This will be a voyage through space and time in search of civilizations older than ours in other parts of the universe. We will look for:

- worlds that exploded their first atomic weapons a million years ago and tamed the base passions that almost turned their planets into bombs;
- worlds of machines that have forgotten the flesh that built them;
- intelligences constructing themselves out of messages sent halfway across the galaxy.

We shall travel to the beginning and end of time. We shall see stars harder than diamonds; hot stars circling each other like dancers bound by rings of fire; titanic explosions that incinerate worlds; and strange dark places that turn reason inside out.

We now think that a man can leave Earth and return a million years later, looking scarcely older than he did when he departed.

We also see that it is not impossible that other beings stopped off here 10 million years ago with plans to return tomorrow, having passed only a few years of their time.

We search the past for records of their visits and the skies for signs of their presence. When four-dozen scientists, mostly American and Soviet, discussed the chances of discovering ETI (Extra-Terrestrial Intelligence) during a week-long conference in Armenia, they decided that at its present stage, Earth technology "may be capable of establishing contact with" ETI, that is, with SuperWorlds.

There are many reasons, as we shall see, for believing we are not the only people in the universe. As a general matter, however, the history of scientific discovery has demonstrated that beliefs that we are ordinary are more likely to be proved correct than beliefs that we are special. And, interestingly, beliefs that we are ordinary result in a more spectacular universe.

Here are some past beliefs in our uniqueness that have been proved wrong:

- Earth is the center of the universe.
- Ours is the only world with a moon.
- Ours is the only sun.
- The time of man is the only time.

Rather than being unique, our sun is a star very much like the other stars we see in the sky. We will examine in some detail, later on, the chances that other stars may be the suns of other Earths or SuperWorlds. For now, it is enough to say that our sun is an ordinary star. If it has circling around it at least one planet on which intelligent life exists, then some of the many billions of other stars also ought to have planets like Earth on which intelligent life exists.

Further, we have found that the age of our sun is about average. This means that there are stars older than the sun and stars younger than the sun. If it has taken an ordinary amount of time for intelligent life to have arisen on a planet of our sun, then suns older

A desire for evidence of space visitors can lead us to find that the prophet Ezekial's vision and other Biblical accounts are records of visits from SuperWorlds. "The man who eagerly awaits the arrival of a friend," an old Chinese proverb says, "should not mistake the beating of his own heart for the thumping hooves of the approaching horse."

than ours must have planets on which intelligent life arose before it did on Earth. If these life-forms lasted any length of time, they probably achieved a higher civilization and greater scientific advance than we have thus far. Their world was, in other words, a SuperWorld.

Whether it still exists is another question. If the SuperWorld is still there, or has been there within the past 50,000 years, we should be able to find it within the next century. If it has been long extinguished, we may still find some signs of it—an old radio beacon still broadcasting signals, an automated probe circling ours, or a nearby sun.

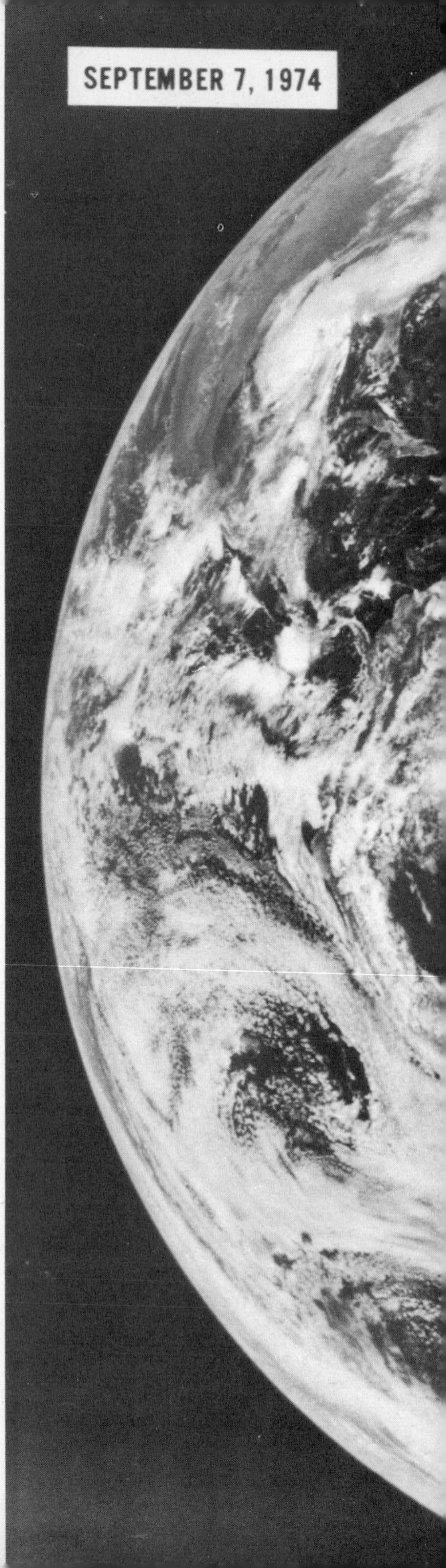


NASA PHOTOGRAPH

Earth, planet of water and clouds. This tiny speck in the black void of space is the nursery of us all. Here life could develop and then change the planet to nurture more life. The air we breathe is as much a creation of living things as our hair and fingernails. Like some great membrane, it divides life from the hostile dark, shielding us from cosmic debris and dangerous rays. We are only beginning to understand the subtle ways in which we and our planet help each other. The miracle may be duplicated elsewhere in the universe, but the web of life is so complicated that we may be sure other creatures will be different. Each Earthling, ant, or astronaut bears the stamp of his origin.

BUREAU OF AMERICAN ETHNOLOGY PHOTOGRAPH

In this thousand-year-old painting from British Honduras can be found a rocket ship, radio vacuum tubes, "space creatures," and a water-cooler containing a head. Are these products of unknown science or the vivid imagination of an unknown artist?

The distances and times involved in this search are enormous by Earthly standards. Here on Earth, the speed of light seems instantaneous. At 186,000 miles a second it can circle the entire planet in about one-eighth of a second. But our galaxy is so large that it takes light tens of thousands of years to travel from one end to the other. Thus, a message from a star on the far side of the galaxy might have originated 80,000 years ago. By the time it reached us, those that sent it—not merely the individuals, but the entire civilization—might have perished. And who would dare guess who will be here 160,000 years from now, when an answer to our answer comes back this way?

Are beings from SuperWorlds here right now, in the vicinity of Earth? Without doubt, some strange objects have been seen in our planet's skies during the past thirty years. "An extraordinary flying object, silvery, metallic, disk-shaped, tens of meters in diameter, and evidently artificial" was witnessed over a farm near McMinnville, Oregon, on May 11, 1950. This account remains one of the few supported by evidence, two photographs that were carefully examined by the staff of the University of Colorado project that investigated UFO's (Unidentified Flying Objects) for the United States Air Force in 1966–68. Another case that survived the group's analysis involved a small light that maneuvered at high speed over an air base in Greenwich, England, in the summer of 1956.

It is also possible that a SuperWorld device was seen by Astronaut James McDivitt during the flight of Gemini 4. On the afternoon of June 4, 1965, while in orbit over the Pacific, McDivitt reported seeing "a cylindrical-shaped object with an antennalike extension . . . that gave a white or silvery appearance as seen against the dark sky." The object seemed to be approaching Gemini 4; and its position did not fit that of any known Earth-launched satellite.

And a young Scottish engineer thinks he has found evidence of a probe from the stars, orbiting our planet in the vicinity of the moon.

A probe from another star system, parked near Earth, could have recorded the Apollo landings and sent a signal home: *New life forms have entered space.*

# 2: Probe From Izar

The mysterious signals were first detected in 1927 by two American radio experimenters. Other messages were received in 1928 and 1929 by Norwegian, Dutch, and French radio engineers. Of course at that time, thirty years before the dawn of the space age, no one conceived that other civilizations might be trying to communicate with us. The signals were recorded, not always completely, and regarded as some kind of puzzling, unexplainable, natural phenomenon.

What made them puzzling was that they appeared to be echoes with varying delay times. A voice echo, for example, is a reflection of the sound waves broadcast by a voice from some surface. The farther this reflecting surface is from the voice-source, the longer it takes for the echo to be heard at the source. At the earth's surface, sound waves travel at a speed of about 1,000 feet per second. Echoes from a surface 1,000 feet from the voice-source would take two seconds to return (one second to get from the source to the reflector, another second to return). Similarly, an echo from a reflector 1 mile away would take ten seconds to return.

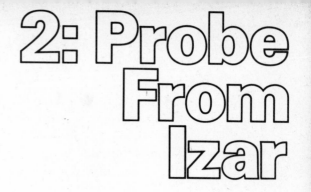

In this way, the time between a sound and its echo could be used to measure the distance of the reflecting surface. This is the method used by bats to navigate in the dark, and it is the principle of sonar.

In the same way, echoes of radio waves can be used to judge the distance of the object reflecting them. This is the principle of radar. In 1927 and 1928, the American and Dutch experimenters, sending signals at short wavelengths, recorded echoes three seconds after their transmissions. Since radio waves, like light, travel at a speed of 186,000 miles a second, the reflected waves must have traveled a distance of 558,000 miles, and whatever was reflecting them was half that distance, or 279,000 miles, from the surface of the earth. This is roughly the distance between the earth and the moon. There was some thought at the time that the signals had been reflected from the moon, but this was dismissed on the grounds that the signal would have become so weak, traveling all that distance, that it could not have been detected when it returned to earth.

On the afternoon of October 11, 1928, the echo times began to vary. At that time, a Norwegian radio engineer, Jörgen Hals, was listening to signals being transmitted from PCJJ, an experimental station operated by the Philips Company, at Eindhoven, Holland. Following the reception of some delayed echoes of Eindhoven signals in 1927, Carl Störmer, a Norwegian mathematician, had asked PCJJ to transmit signals at the 31.4 meter wavelength several times a week. At half-past three in the afternoon of October 11, Hals began getting very clear echoes and, what was very puzzling, noticed that the delay times varied greatly. He called Störmer on the telephone, and within a few minutes the mathematician was at his house where, from three forty-five until four, they recorded four sequences of delayed echoes.

PCJJ, in Eindhoven, was sending three dots in rapid succession, twenty seconds apart, and the echoes were coming back at different times, varying from three seconds to fifteen seconds. Hals and Störmer didn't know what to make of this. If these were indeed echoes, it meant that whatever was reflecting the signals was changing its distance from the earth between signals. A three-second echo meant it was as far away as the moon. The next echo, ten seconds, meant it was more than three times as far away, about 900,000 miles from Earth. The next, seven seconds, indicated that it had moved a quarter-of-a-million miles closer. What was even more puzzling was that the signals showed no sign that the reflecting surface was moving. A moving surface would change the frequency (and wavelength) of the signal, just as sound from an approaching source appears to rise as it approaches and to descend as it moves farther away. This "Doppler effect" would have moved the signals away from the 31.4 meter wavelength to which Hals's radio was tuned, distorting the echoes and forcing him to retune his set to catch them.

This did not happen. Neither did the echoes vary in loudness, which they should have were their distance from the Earth changing. Hals and Störmer had to conclude that the source of the echoes was stationary.

Startled and puzzled, Hals and Störmer telephoned Van der Pol, the engineer in charge of the Philips station, and asked him to transmit more signals that night. Van der Pol left an interval of 30 seconds between signals to make it easier to detect the echoes. With a stopwatch, Störmer recorded a series of echoes with the following delays in seconds: 8, 11, 15, 8, 13, 3, 8, 8, 8, 12, 15, 13, 8, 8. Except for the 3-second echo, which came back clearly in the form of three dots, the echoes were blurred into dashes.

Two weeks later, on October 24, a sequence of forty-eight echoes was recorded in Oslo. Other radio experimenters in England and Norway heard delayed echoes several times during early 1929, but none left records like those of Störmer and Van der Pol, until May, when two French scientists went to Indochina to study the effects of an eclipse of the sun on radio transmission. J. B. Galle and G. Talon transmitted two dots every thirty seconds at a wavelength of 25 meters. (Van der Pol had transmitted at 31.4 meters.) The dots were at different musical frequencies (notes on the scale). This, in effect, gave each signal a signature so that, were echoes heard, there would be no question as to which signal had caused it. Echoes were recorded by two observers, one listening to a speaker, the other to headphones. Altogether, they recorded three long echo sequences with varying delays over a three-day period.

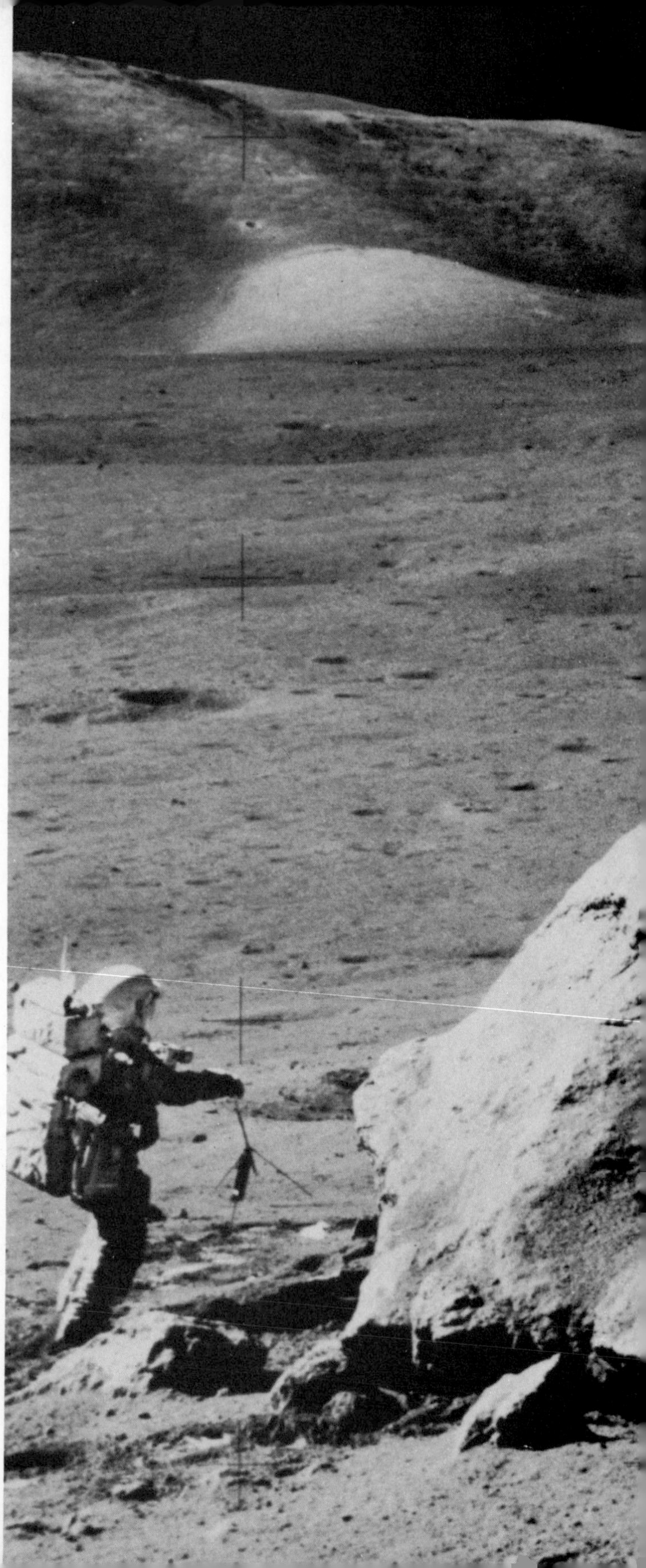

NASA PHOTOGRAPH

The Moon is the first other world reached by mankind, the beginning of a great adventure. One thing we have learned from our explorations is that it resembles the Earth of 3 billion years ago. Earth, however, went on to make an atmosphere, an ocean, and continents.

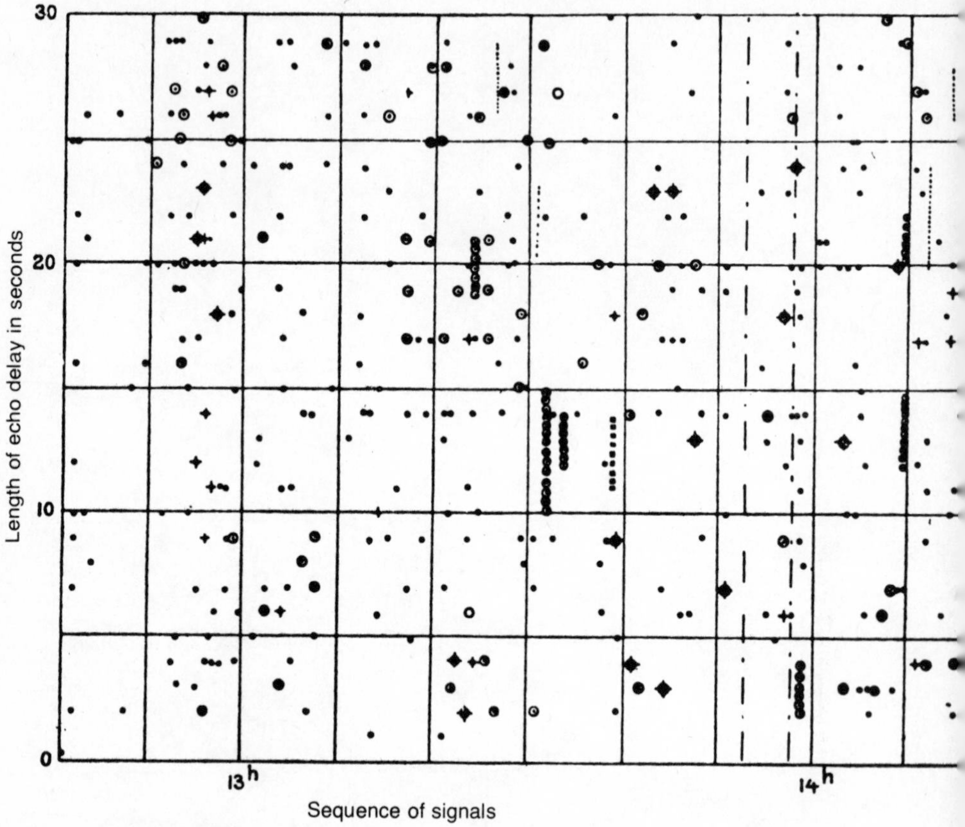


Trying to make sense out of the signals they received in May, 1929, the Frenchmen, Galle and Talon, made this chart. The small dots are weak echoes; the large dots, strong ones. Is there a message here from a SuperWorld?

During this experiment something quite remarkable happened. The operator forgot to send two of the signals, but echoes came nevertheless, timed at five and ten seconds after the times the two forgotten signals should have been transmitted. Another difference between these echoes and those detected from the Dutch transmissions, was that some came only one or two seconds after the signals, whereas the shortest delay time noted by Störmer, Hals, and Van der Pol was three seconds.

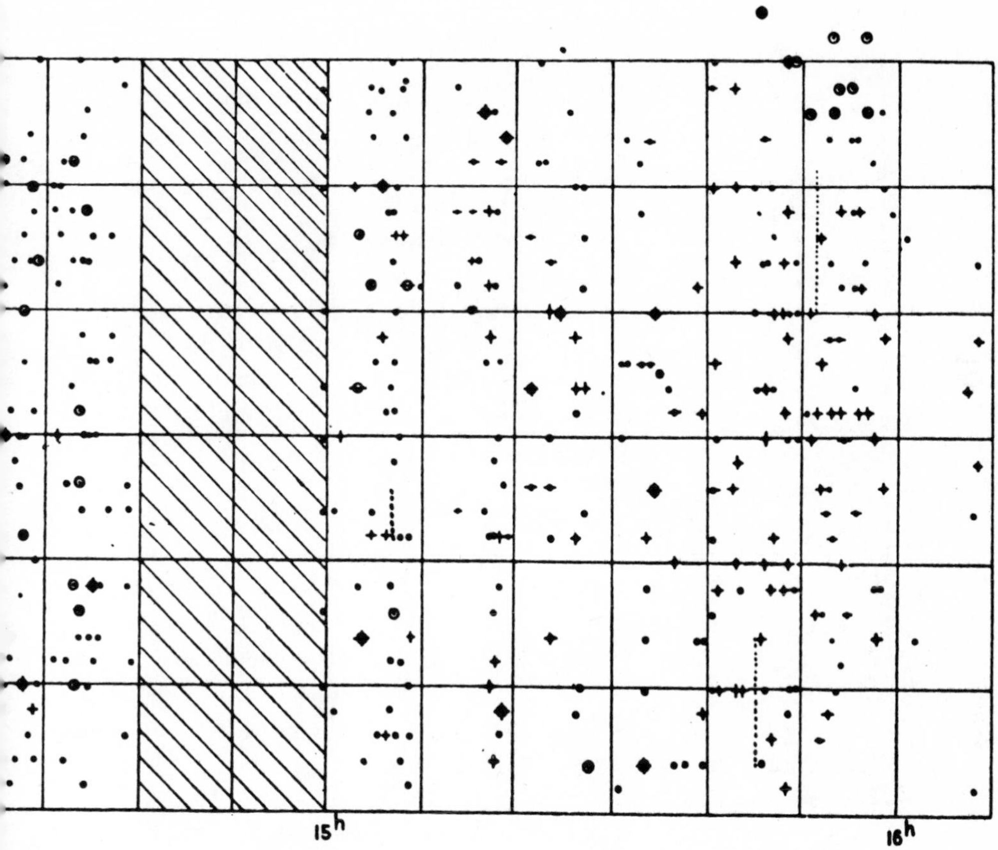


All these sequences of echoes were described in scientific journals at the time, the Störmer and Van der Pol records appearing in the British publication *Nature* and the *Proceedings of the Royal Society of Edinburgh;* and those of Galle and Talon in *L'Onde Electrique* (*The Electric Wave*). Störmer theorized that they were caused by reflections from the inside of a hollow shell of electric particles surrounding the earth and trapped by its magnetic field. The delay times varied, he said, as the transmitted waves took different paths around the earth, bouncing along the insides of these electrical shells. There was no way, at the time, of proving or disproving this explanation, and the records remained half-forgotten curiosities of early radio experiments.

In 1960, Ronald N. Bracewell, an Australian radio-astronomer at Stanford University, California, suggested in an article in *Nature* that the best way for us to contact superior civilizations would be to look for probes sent by them to monitor our solar system. Just as we have sent Mariner and Pioneer vessels as the most practical and inexpensive way to explore the planets of our solar system, interstellar probes sent from one star system to another would be the most practical way of looking for other civilizations.

An intersteller probe, Bracewell argued, would be solar powered to last a long time, and programmed to orbit a star at about the distance from it that one would expect to find a habitable planet, based on the star's heat output. It would listen for signs of civilization, have a way to respond to make its presence known, and would probably have a computer capable of supplying considerable information.

"The probe could first listen for our signals," Bracewell wrote, "and then repeat them back. To us, its signals would have the appearance of echoes having delays of seconds or minutes, such as were reported thirty years ago by Störmer and Van der Pol and never explained."

Bracewell also suggested that the probe might begin its communication with a television picture of a constellation. In 1972, Duncan A. Lunan, of Troon, Ayrshire, Scotland, a young graduate of Glasgow University, began a study of the old Hals, Störmer, and Van der Pol echo sequences, with Bracewell's ideas in mind.

Bracewell had suggested that the first transmission would be a television picture of a constellation. A television picture is a mosaic of bright and dark dots on a series of parallel lines. In American television, 525 lines, each consisting of hundreds of dots, are transmitted in 1/30 second. But any other number of lines, any other number of dots, or speed, could be used to make a picture. The problem in making a picture out of a signal sent by a strange transmitter is to figure out the system used. This is called the "raster." It is to a television picture what a frame is to any other kind of picture. An alien spaceship, for example, not knowing the raster of American television, might think we were sending pictures consisting of 105 lines in 1/150 second. From this they would get pictures 5 times as long as they should be, and 1/5 as high. The image would look as if a photograph had been cut horizontally into five equal strips, which were then pasted end to end. The aliens would have to experiment with different rasters until they found the one that gave coherent pictures.

This is what Duncan Lunan did with the signals heard in 1928. When he assumed that each of the equally spaced signals transmitted by PCJJ was used to represent a different line in the television picture, and that the delay times were indications of the position of the dot in the line, he found that the echo sequence of the night of October 11 made a crude picture, as shown on page 18. He used this sequence because it had been recorded in two places, both at Eindhoven and at Oslo, which ruled out any chance that the delays were somehow originating in the receiving equipment.

Studying this picture, Lunan decided that all the dots at eight-second delay represented some kind of reference line. Then, consulting a star atlas, he decided that the dots to the right of the reference line came closest to matching the northern hemisphere constellation Boötes. A few things were wrong, however. The two brightest stars in the constellation were missing, as were three of four duller, but equal-appearing, stars in the constellation's southwest corner.

On the other hand, there was an extra dot to the north of where Arcturus belonged, and another "echo" all by itself to the left of the vertical reference line. This separate dot was distinguished from all the others in another way. Whereas all the others had been blurred, as received in Holland and Norway, this signal had come back exactly as it had been transmitted, in the form of three dots.

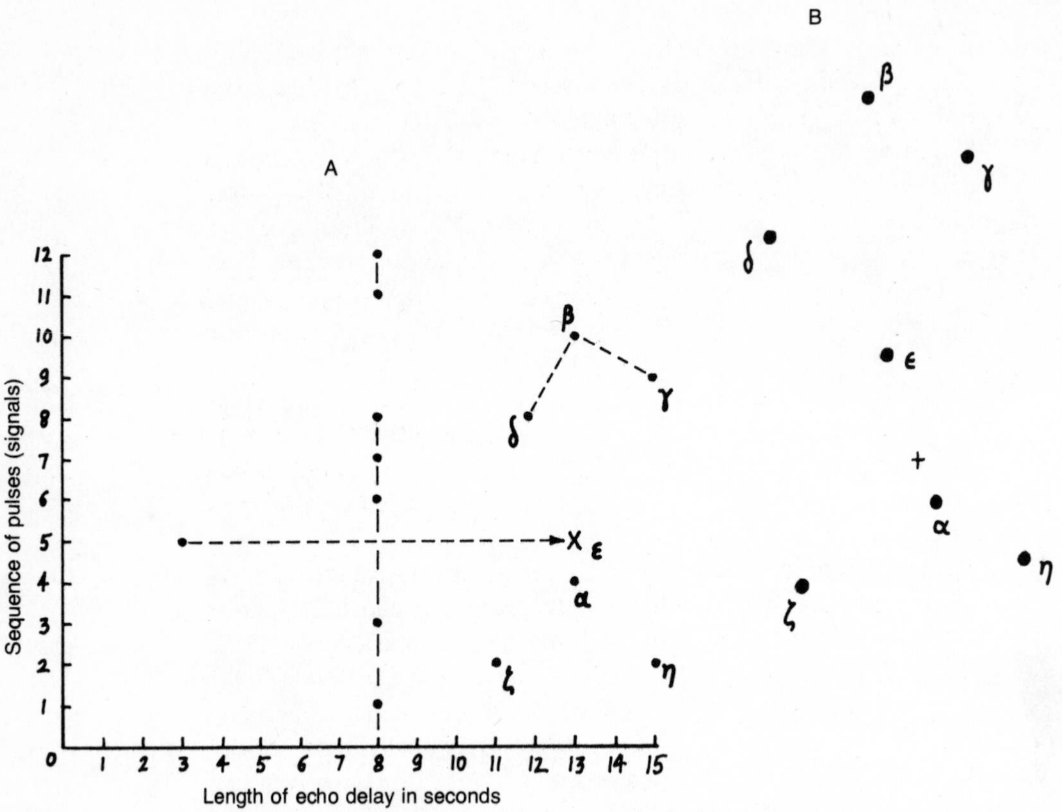


(A) prepared by Lunan from the Van der Pol records of October 11, 1928. Compare the figure, composed of six dots, with the constellation Boötes, in (B), taken from a star atlas. The $\alpha$ indicates Arcturus. The + in (B) shows where Arcturus was 13,000 years ago. The X in (A) shows where Epsilon Boötes should have been.

The lone dot was at position 3 in Lunan's picture, representing a three-second delay. It was thus five seconds (or units) to the left of the reference line. It occurred to Lunan that if it were moved five units to the right of the reference line, it would be at position 13, which was precisely where Epsilon Boötes, one of the missing stars, belonged.

The picture, then, Lunan reasoned, was not quite that of a constellation. It was a question: Do you know where this star (Epsilon Boötes) belongs? Lunan thinks that had PCJJ then transmitted back a signal repeating the entire delay sequence but changing the fifth pulse from three-second delay to thirteen, the probe would then have sent additional information.

Assuming this interpretation was correct, this still left Arcturus in the wrong place. All the stars have random motions with respect to one another. Some move faster than others. Generally, the closer they are to the sun, the more noticeable their motion as seen from Earth. The discrepancy in Arcturus's position, Lunan found, could be explained by the fact that Arcturus is one of the stars nearest the sun and moves rather quickly through the sky, compared with other stars. Since the direction in which it is moving is south, the picture showed Arcturus in the position it had occupied 13,000 years ago. Lunan understood this to mean that the probe had arrived in our solar system at that time and had not bothered to correct its picture since.

Applying similar methods to other echo sequences, Lunan found other pictures that could be interpreted as constellations as they appeared 13,000 years ago. The most extensive records, those of Galle and Talon, involved hundreds of echoes. The two French scientists had themselves tried to make sense out of them, drawing elaborate charts not very different from those in which Lunan found his constellations. They seemed to be full of information, and Lunan spent a long time puzzling over them. His belief that they represented intelligent signals was strengthened by the strange quirks the Frenchmen had noted. That the "echoes" arrived even when two signals had not been transmitted indicated to Lunan that they could not have been mere passive reflections. The less-than-three-second delay times he took as evidence that the probe, having digested the Frenchmen's system of sending signals at thirty-second intervals, was simply using this as the basis for sending them its coded information. The problem, Lunan felt, was in understanding the code. What was the meaning of strong and weak signals? Here was a message from the stars if only he could grasp it.

At one point he thought the probe had originated on the sixth of seven planets circling one of the two stars we call Epsilon Boötes.

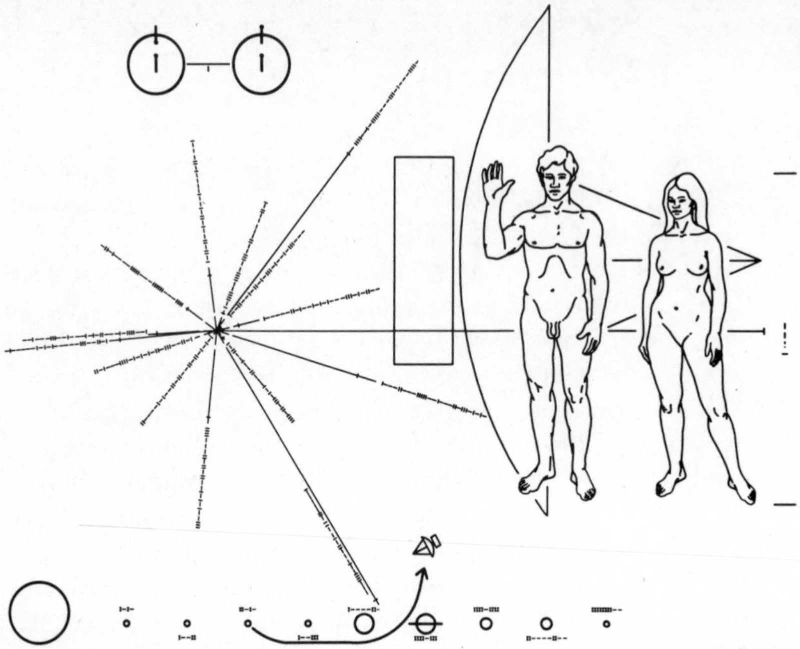

NASA PHOTOGRAPH

The first attempt to communicate with a SuperWorld. This message, on board Pioneer 10, gives the probe's home as the third planet of a star whose address is indicated in terms of pulsars. It also tells something about us.

The double star Epsilon Boötes lies more than 200 light years from the sun. Also known by the names Izar and Pulcherrima, its two stars circle each other at a distance of some 8 billion * miles. For comparison, the family of planets surrounding our sun extends to a distance of 3.6 billion miles, the orbit of Pluto. If our sun were part of a similar double-star system, its campanion would appear to us as a bright star, brighter than the full moon.

Is it possible that planets circle either Izar or Pulcherrima, and that one of them spawned a civilization that launched a probe that arrived here 13,000 years ago, when the last Ice Age was ending and mankind knew only stone and bone for the making of tools?

To answer that question we shall have to travel backward in time to the very beginning of things, to the origin of the universe.

Then we shall return to Mr. Lunan and his puzzle from the stars.

* 1 billion in this book means one thousand million.

# 3: The Galaxy, From AU to Kiloparsec

No one on this planet knows the age of the universe. To determine its age, we would have to know when it began. We do not know with any certainty if, in fact, it had a beginning.

We explore the universe for clues. Fortunately it is full of electromagnetic (EM) radiation and we have sense organs—eyes—sensitive to some of it. Light, perceived by our eyes, is a form of EM radiation. This radiation travels at a very high speed and can be detected over enormous distances. It brings us all the information we have on what lies beyond our planet. It is marvelous that our eyes, evolved for survival on this little planet, have brought us into contact with the universe beyond it. With our naked eyes we can see as far as 2 million light years into space, which is the same as seeing 2 million years back into time. Instruments increase this range manyfold.

The speed of light is about 186,000 miles per second. This speed tells us something, by no means completely understood, about the nature of our universe. First of all, it is the speed limit of the universe. Nothing can travel faster. And, strangely, it seems that its speed remains the same under all conditions.

In the ordinary world we can add speeds. A stone thrown forward from a moving car travels faster than a stone thrown by a man standing at the side of the road. The speed of the car is added to the speed of the stone. This is not true of light. A ray of light from an Apollo capsule leaving the earth at 7 miles a second will not have a velocity any different from light from a capsule standing on its launching pad. This constancy of the speed of light was one of the discoveries that destroyed the fabric of our understanding of the universe at the end of the nineteenth century. A new fabric had to be woven, and this was largely the work of Albert Einstein.

In a universe of constant—invariant—light speed, many things happen that defy common sense. This is because common sense is based on speeds very much slower than the speed of light. The strange things in Einstein's new universe become noticeable only at very high speeds. In Einstein's universe, things that in the common-sense world seem distinct and separate start blending together. Matter and energy become interchangeable, and matter and space, and even space and time. As we shall see later on, these features of the universe have an important bearing on our plans for exploration and our concept of what SuperWorlds may have achieved.

For now, however, it is important to consider only the invariance of the speed of light, for from that we can construct rods to measure the universe.

We use light to measure the universe in many ways. And not only do we use light, but the rest of the EM spectrum as well. Radio waves are a form of EM radiation, so are x-rays, heat rays, and the dangerous high-energy gamma rays from radioactive decay. All these different forms of EM radiation travel at the same speed, 186,000 miles a second. What distinguishes one from another is its wavelength. Light, the part of the EM spectrum we see, has wavelengths going from .000039 centimeters (deep violet) to .000076 centimeters (dark red). Our eyes are able to sense waves in lengths of this range and to detect different wavelengths, which we see as different colors. Waves .00005 centimeters in length appear to us as blue, and those .000055 centimeters long, as green, and so on. Below red, as the waves get longer, we have infrared (heat) and radio (from .003 centimeters to about 25 kilometers, or 15 miles). The waves that Van der Pol was broadcasting from station PCJJ in Holland in 1928 were 31.4 meters (99 feet) long. At the other end of the visible part of the spectrum we go to ultraviolet, then to x-rays, which have wavelengths as short as .00000004 centimeters, to gamma rays with wavelengths only one ten-millionth as long as violet light. This very short wave EM radiation begins to act more like particles with mass than waves, and we start getting into one of the areas in which the new physics defies our everyday ideas based on our crude senses; for just as matter becomes energy and energy becomes matter, particles become waves and waves become particles.

Much has been learned of the universe by breaking down the light from distant objects into its component wavelengths. A rainbow is sunlight broken into component wavelengths by rain drops. Similarly, a glass prism can be used to make an artificial rainbow, or spectrum. When heated, atoms give off characteristic wavelengths. Thus the spectrum of light from a star can reveal the atoms it is made of. Also the Doppler principle—wavelengths seem to be shorter as the source of the waves approaches the observer, and longer as the source recedes from the observer—reveals the motions of stars and other objects.

What is the picture of the universe that emerges from examinations of x-rays, light, and infrared and radio waves coming to us from the far reaches of the universe? In the first place, the universe is so enormous as to defy understanding. Starting with our immediate neighborhood, where distances are still comprehensible, planet Earth is 93 million miles from the sun. For convenience, this distance is called an Astronomical Unit, AU. The sun has at least nine planets in orbit around it, as well as small bits of rock, hundreds of thousands of small planets (up to 400 miles in diameter), dust, and millions of comets.

The most distant known planet, Pluto, is about 40 AUs from the sun. Beyond Pluto there are comets out to a distance of perhaps

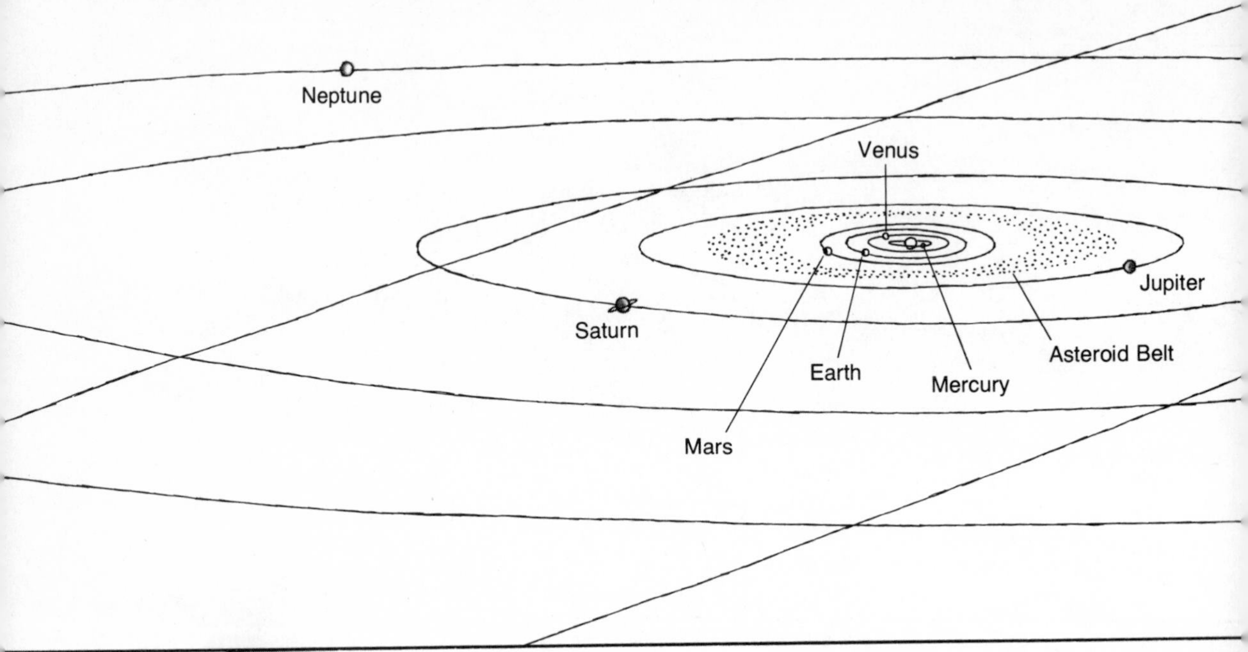
Neptune
Venus
Jupiter
Saturn
Asteroid Belt
Earth
Mercury
Mars

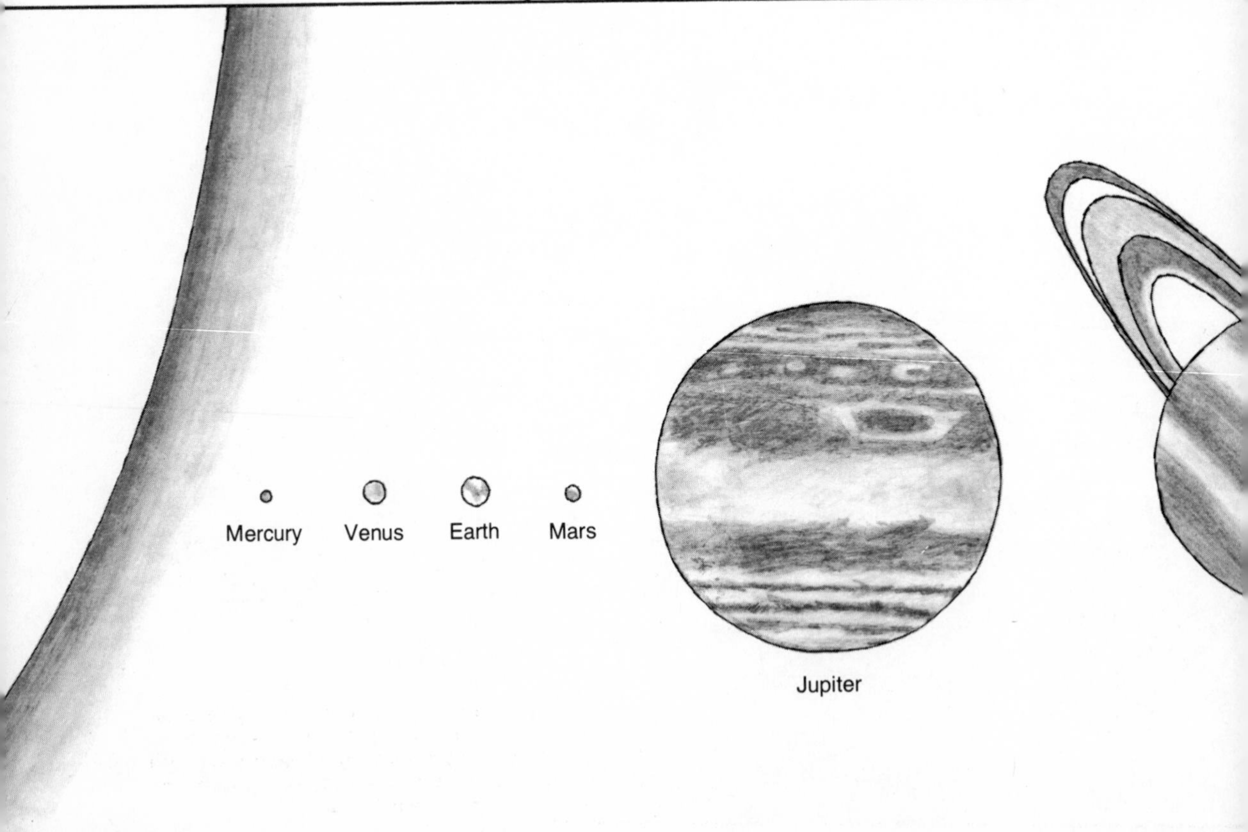
Mercury
Venus
Earth
Mars
Jupiter

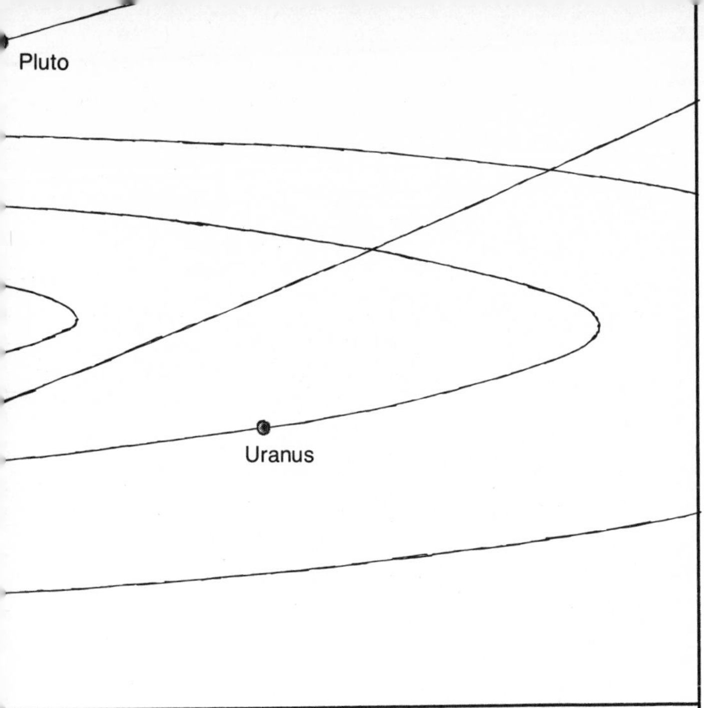


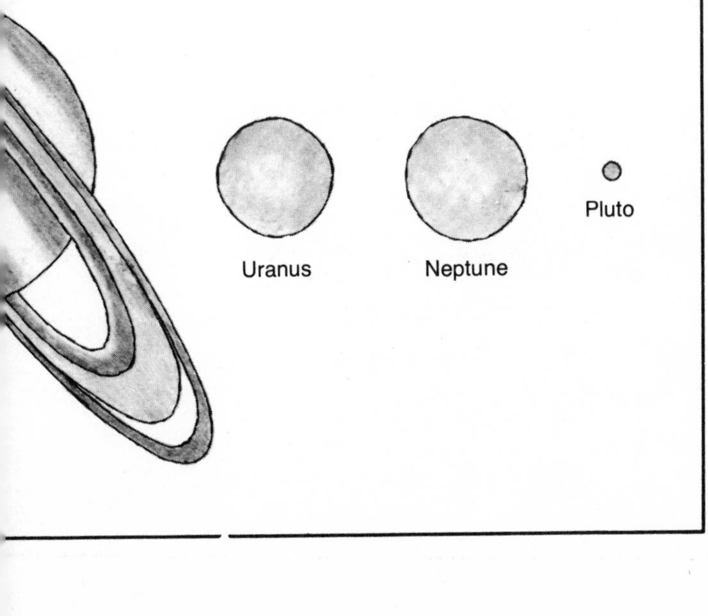


Starships from other worlds may have visited our system many times. We have only just begun to explore it ourselves. Who knows what wonders we may find on some moon of Uranus?

100,000 AUs. The distance to the nearest detected star is about 260,000 AUs. This star is the constellation Centaurus in the southern sky.

We can see that the Astronomical Unit (AU), which seemed quite large, is becoming too small to be useful in measuring distances between stars. We need a much larger unit, the parsec. A parsec is the distance traveled by light in about three and a quarter years. In one year, light covers about 63,000 AUs, so a parsec will be equal to about 200,000 AUs. Measured in parsecs, the distance to the star in the Centaur will be 1.3. It is easier to talk about 1.3 parsecs than about 260,000 AUs.

There is some uncertainty about the number of stars in the neighborhood of our sun. We have detected twenty-two within 4 parsecs, nine hundred within 20 parsecs, and three thousand within 30 parsecs; but some astronomers are beginning to think there may be a great many more faint small stars around, perhaps ten times as many as we think. This is the reason why we cannot be sure that Alpha Centauri, the triple-star system in the Centaur, is (*are,* since there are three stars) the closest to us.

To visualize our sun with respect to its neighbors, imagine a baseball diamond. If we put our sun at home plate, and make the distance from earth to sun (an AU) a hundredth of an inch, then Pluto, the outermost known planet, will be a little less than half an inch from the sun. There will be a kind of mist of comets wheeling around about as far from home plate as the pitcher's mound and extending all around the sun to the backstop, the mist reaching a height of 60 feet over home plate. Scattered over the playing field will be twenty-two tiny points of light, each with its own large mist of comets and each representing a star. The stars known to be closest to the sun, Alpha Centauri, will be in short centerfield.

Thinly scattered in this manner, grains of bright dust in the black sea of space, are millions of other stars extending for vast distances beyond. They are not, however, scattered at random. As we examine more and more of them, not just the nearest twenty-two, but the nearest few thousand, we find certain patterns.

Spherical clouds of comets, surrounding their suns at great distances, may provide stepping stones to the stars. They may provide us with the fuel we need to roam the galaxy and also with exotic habitats (see page 138).

Our sun and its neighbors are part of a great system of stars wheeling in space. This system, called the Milky Way Galaxy, is shaped like a lens. It contains, altogether, about 250 billion stars. There is a concentration of stars in a central sphere, and a disk of stars in the plane of its equator.

Our sun is about a third of the distance from the outer edge of the galaxy, in the disk, in a long river of stars spiraling away from the center.

Since we are now getting involved with distances very much greater than those in our immediate neighborhood, we shall again have to shift to a bigger unit—the kiloparsec, equal to 1,000 parsecs.

The galaxy is about 33 kiloparsecs in diameter. The disk is flattened to about half a kiloparsec in thickness. The central sphere of stars is about 5 kiloparsecs in diameter. The total amount of mass in the galaxy is calculated to be about 100 billion times that of our sun. Most of this is concentrated in the central sphere, which is so thick with stars that were we to be located there instead of in the outer part of the disk, the night sky would be as bright as two hundred full moons.

A

HALE OBSERVATORIES PHOTOGRAPH

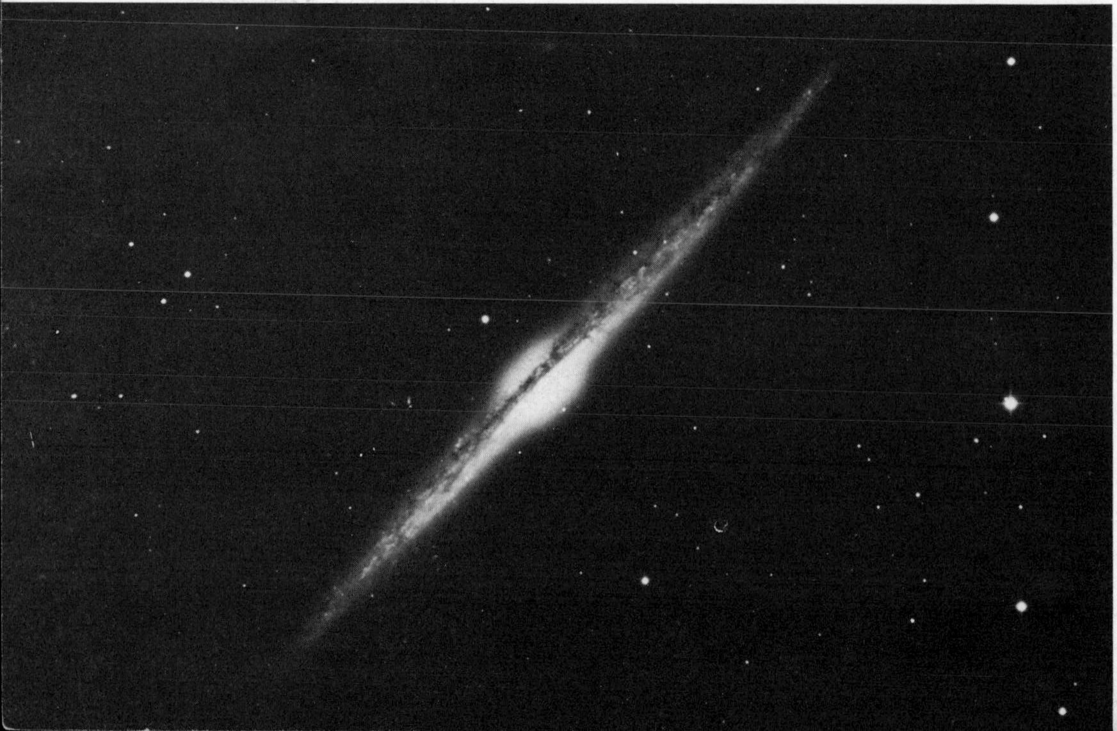

B

HALE OBSERVATORIES PHOTOGRAPH

Photographs of three other galaxies show what ours would look like if it were seen from three different angles: (A) edge on—the equator, (B) from about 30° above the equator, (C) from the top—north pole.

HALE OBSERVATORIES PHOTOGRAPH

C

HALE OBSERVATORIES PHOTOGRAPH

Astronomers have found, floating among the stars of our galaxy, formaldehyde (which can become sugar), hydrocyanic acid (which can become purines), and cyanoacetylene (which can become pyramidines). The purines and pyramidines are the stuff from which DNA, the organizer of life, is composed (see Chapter 7).

The concentration of stars in the central sphere rises toward the core. Were our sun in the core instead of in the galactic outskirts, we would have one-hundred thousand stars within 4 parsecs, instead of twenty-two.

The galaxy, like everything in this universe—our solar system, the sun, the Earth, Earth's moon, the fundamental particles of matter of which all else is composed—rotates on an axis.

Rivers of stars stream outward from the galactic core in long, unwinding spiral arms. In our little corner of space, about 10 kiloparsecs from the galactic core, the arms are spaced about 2 kiloparsecs apart. Our sun is located along the outer edge of the second of the three arms. It moves around the center, with its family of planets, comets, and asteroids, at a speed of 160 miles a second, making one circuit of the galaxy every 200 million years.

The time the sun takes to go around the galaxy, 200 million years, is the galactic year, a time unit we shall find useful as we follow events through our galaxy's history.

HALE OBSERVATORIES PHOTOGRAPH

The night sky as seen from a world close to the core of the galaxy. This is actually the center of our twin galaxy in the constellation Andromeda, seen through a high-powered telescope.

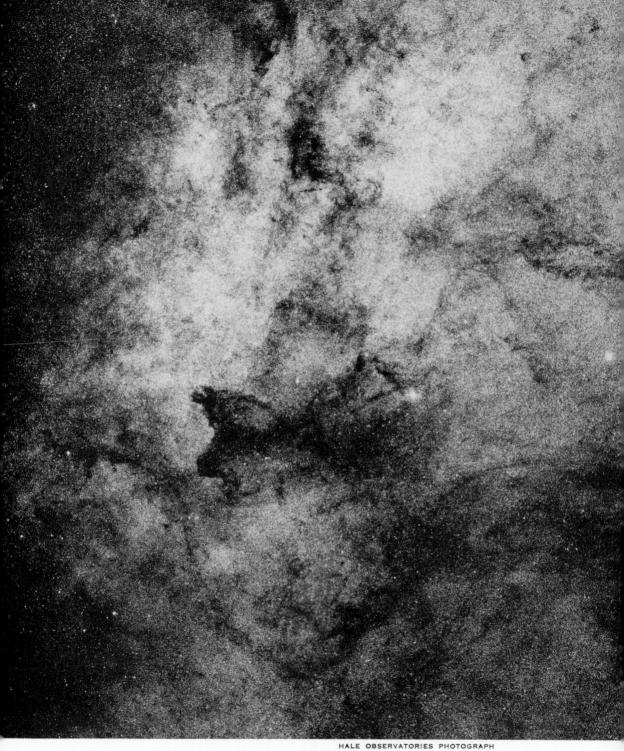

Farther from the core, the hold of the center lessens, so that beyond 16 kiloparsecs things seem to break away from the galaxy. Stars and dust and clouds of gas race out toward other galaxies while enormous amounts of hydrogen—enough to make 500 suns—flow into the galactic core, where all sorts of mysterious things are taking place.

The center of our galaxy is in the direction of the constellation Sagittarius, where the Milky Way crosses it low in the summer sky. The shape of our galaxy and our location in it have not been easy to figure out. The problem has been something like trying to map a forest of unknown shape while spending one's entire life somewhere within it, beside a single tree. The Milky Way that stretches across the sky is our galaxy, the vicinity of the equatorial plane where stars lie thick along the spiral arms, seen edgeways. The view is imperfect, for dust clouds obscure much of it, shielding from our eyes the core of the galaxy, among other things.

We have seen the core with the radio part of the EM spectrum, and it may be just as well that only one ten-thousandth of the visible light from there reaches us. It seems likely that the core explodes every 500 million years with a force equal to all the energy locked up in a hundred thousand suns, and that other violent and as yet unknown events occur there all the time. The core may be a birthplace of matter, a cemetery of time, a gateway to other universes. There are things to be learned there that will change our ideas about everything we know.

And . . . beyond the galaxy? We shall now voyage beyond our nursery of 250 billion stars.

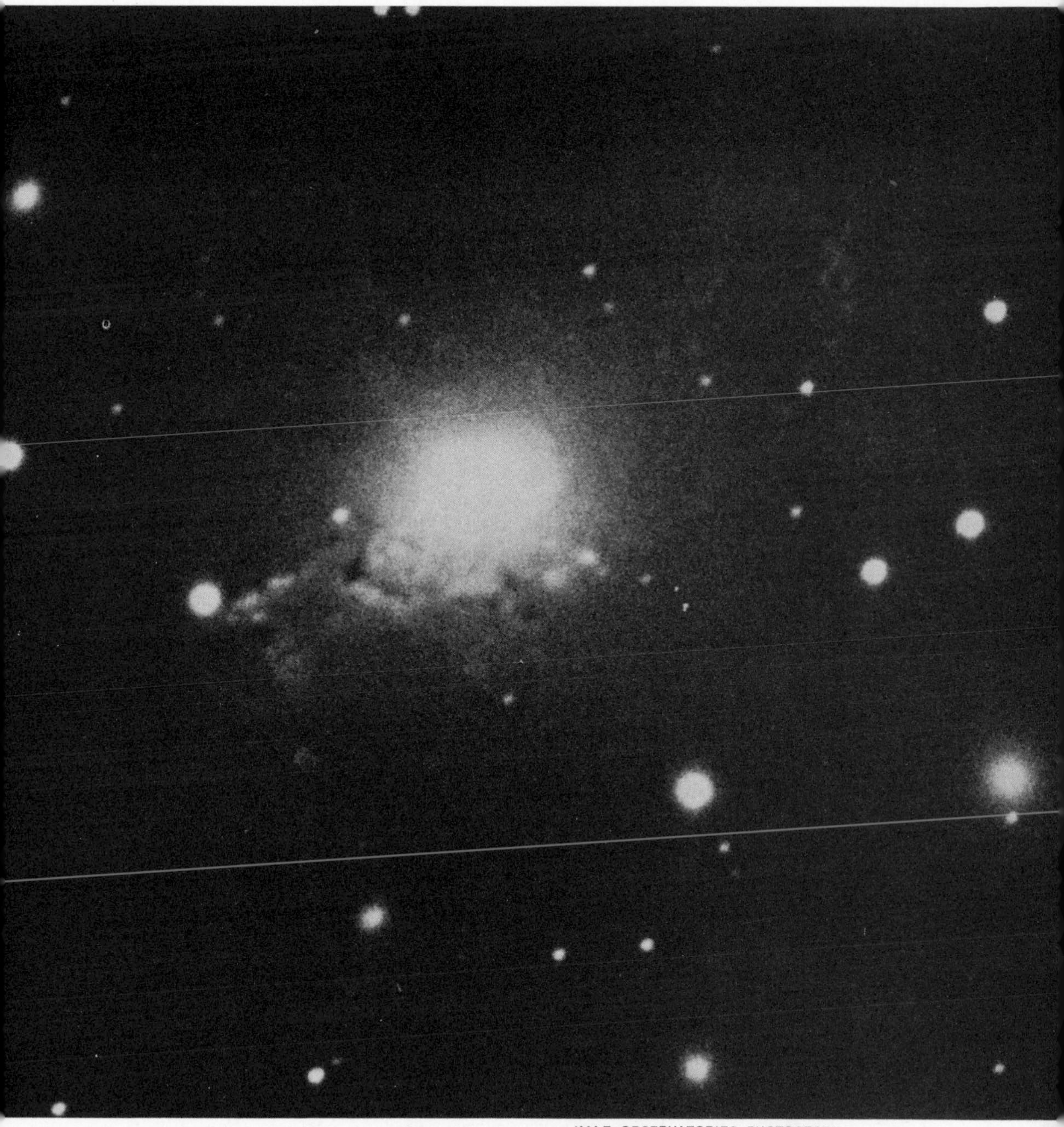

HALE OBSERVATORIES PHOTOGRAPH

An explosion in the center of this galaxy is expelling an enormous amount of matter, enough to make another small galaxy.

# 4: The Universe

Deep in the southern sky are what appear to be two small, detached pieces of the Milky Way. These are two small galaxies, the Magellenic Clouds, 48 and 56 kiloparsecs away. In the northern sky, a faint blur of light in the constellation Andromeda is resolved by a telescope into a lens-shaped object composed of billions of stars. This is another big galaxy like our own. It is over 600 kiloparsecs distant. Within a thousand kiloparsecs of our galaxy there are, in addition to the Magellenic Clouds and the big galaxy in Andromeda, sixteen other galaxies.

Other groups of galaxies stand farther off in space, and as we look at them we shall, finally, be looking at the universe as a whole. To do this, though, again requires a larger unit of measurement, for as we have seen, even within our little local group of galaxies we are talking in terms of 1,000 kiloparsecs; 1,000 kiloparsecs is 1 megaparsec, our unit for discussing the universe.

We have climbed a long way from the Astronomical Unit (AU), useful within the solar system, to the megaparsec, useful in the universe. To look back a moment before going on, the distance of 1 yard is to the AU, what the AU is to the megaparsec.

LICK OBSERVATORY PHOTOGRAPH

The large Magellenic Cloud, a small galaxy, is quite near our own. It may be formed of matter spewed out by an explosion in our galaxy's core.

HALE OBSERVATORIES PHOTOGRAPH

Our galaxy from 50 kiloparsecs out in deep space. (Actually our twin galaxy in Andromeda, seen through a telescope.)

HALE OBSERVATORIES PHOTOGRAPH

System of galaxies in the constellation Hercules.

There are billions of galaxies in the universe, perhaps as many as there are stars in our galaxy. The groups of galaxies, sometimes consisting of hundreds of galaxies, are megaparsecs apart. The most distant objects we have detected emit so much energy that we cannot explain them with what we know of physical laws. Known as quasars (quasi-stellar objects), the farthest yet found is about 3,000 megaparsecs away. Since it takes light 10 billion years to travel 3,000 megaparsecs, this quasar, 4C 534, appears to us as it was 10 billion years ago. Since it is not much bigger than our solar system, some astronomers think it may represent a state all galaxies were in 10 billion years ago.

All galaxies are in motion. Our local group of twenty galaxies seems to be moving at about 360 miles per second toward a place in the southern sky between the constellations Hydra and the Southern Cross. The American astronomer Edwin P. Hubble found that all the groups of galaxies are racing apart at velocities that increase as their distances from one another increase, at something between 30 and 70 miles per second per megaparsec. This velocity, known as the Hubble Constant, has not been exactly determined, but taking a middle estimate, 50 miles per second per megaparsec, we find the cluster of galaxies in the constellation Virgo, 11 or so megaparsecs distant, speeding away at a rate of 700 miles per second. Galaxies ten times farther away would be going at 7,000 miles per second, and quasar 4C 534, about 3,000 megaparsecs out, has a speed of 150,000 miles per second.

Recession of the galaxies is one of the strangest things man has detected. We can't observe it directly; we get data on our instruments that tell us this must be happening. The data are the light from distant galaxies, which we analyze. In the spectra of light from galaxies, the lines that identify elements are always moved toward the red end of the spectrum. That is, they appear to be longer waves than we would expect them to be. This is known as the "red shift." The most logical explanation for this effect is that their source is in motion away from us. According to the Doppler principle, as a source of waves recedes from an observer, its waves appear to be longer.

Not only do all the spectra from other groups of galaxies show this reddening, but the farther away they are (their distances judged by other means), the greater the red shift. Also, we have never found a single galactic spectrum shifted toward the other, violet, end of the rainbow, which would indicate that the galaxy was coming toward us.

In other words, if the Doppler explanation of the red shift is correct, all the other groups of galaxies are moving away from us, and the farther away they are, the faster they are moving. Does this mean that our own group of galaxies suffers from some sort of plague that all the others are escaping? Also, if in every direction we look, we find all the galaxies moving away, does this mean that we are in the center of the universe, in a special place after all?



HALE OBSERVATORIES PHOTOGRAPH
Cluster of five galaxies. The detection of formaldehyde in other galaxies shows that life is as possible there as in our own galaxy.

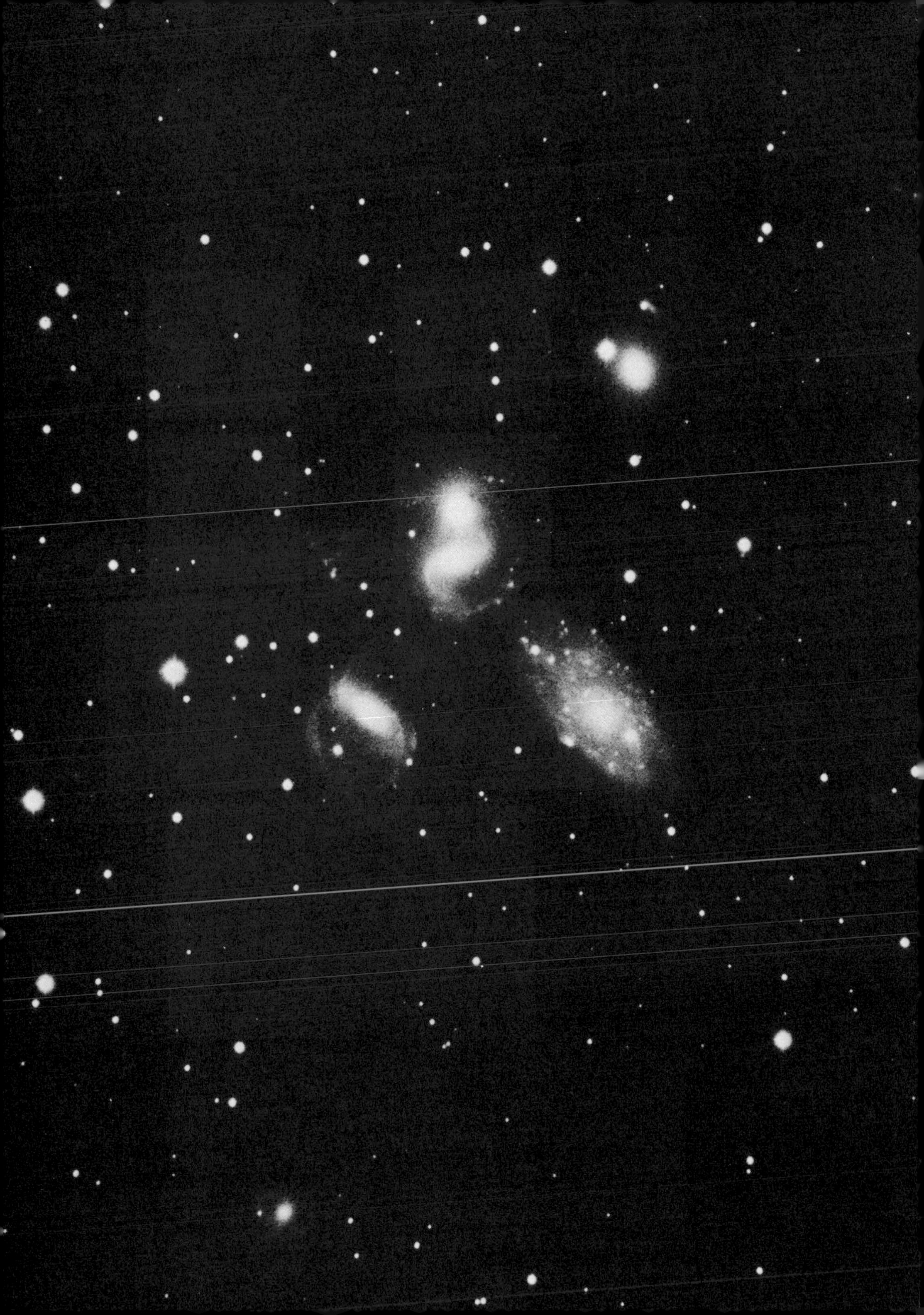

HALE OBSERVATORIES PHOTOGRAPH

What is happening, it seems, is that the entire universe is growing, just as if it had nibbled a magic mushroom. Imagine that the room you are in is growing, but in a special way. All the objects in the room, including you and the furniture, stay the same size. Only the room itself grows, its walls, floors, and ceilings all receding from each other and increasing the distances between all the objects in the room. What would you see? As the room doubled in each dimension—from 12 to 24 feet long, from 10 to 20 feet wide, from 8 to 16 feet high—the distances would double. But the effect of the doubling would be greater, the farther away from you an object

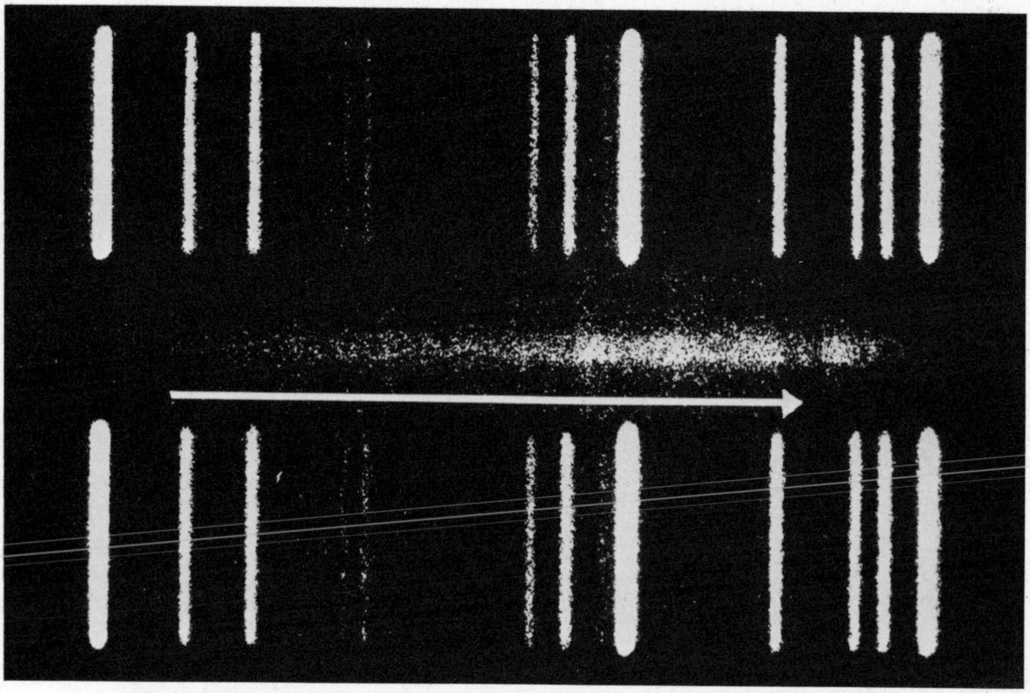

HALE OBSERVATORIES PHOTOGRAPH

The fuzzy line above the arrow is the spectrum of the galaxy on page 40. The dark gap at the head of the arrow corresponds with the dark gap in the spectrum shown at the top and bottom of the picture. Its displacement to the right indicates the speed of the galaxy—38,000 miles a second.

had been in the first place. A lamp next to your chair that was originally 1 foot away, would now be 2 feet away. But the picture on the wall, formerly 5 feet away, would now be 10 feet away, and the fireplace at the other end of the room would have increased its distance from 9 to 18 feet. The lamp moved 1 foot while the picture moved 5 feet and the fireplace moved 9 feet. The farther away from you an object was to begin with, the farther it has moved. This is the same as saying that the picture has moved five times as fast as the lamp and that the fireplace has moved nine times as fast as the lamp.

Furthermore, objects would appear to have receded from you in whichever direction you looked. (You must imagine that your room is in outer space, where gravity is negligible, so that the floor

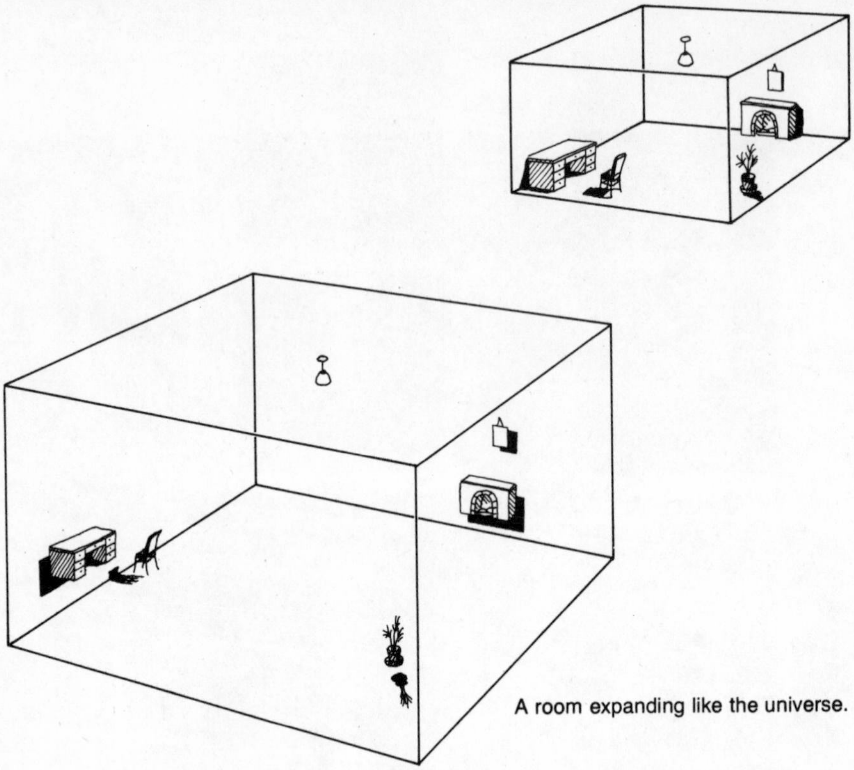

A room expanding like the universe.

has moved away from your feet too.) The effect would be the same, no matter where you were in the room.

Now, returning to the universe, we can see that the recession of galaxies at speeds that increased with distance can be explained by the fact that the universe is expanding.

From the observed rate of expansion, we can easily calculate the rate at which the universe is growing. If the galaxies in Virgo, for example, are receding at the rate of 700 miles per second, then the time it will take them to double their distance from 11 to 22 megaparsecs comes to about 10 billion years. Furthermore, we can calculate that the universe is adding volume at the rate of about 200 cubic megaparsecs a year, or enough space to accommodate several groups of galaxies like our own.

This doubling time has another, much more interesting, significance. If the Virgo cluster would move an additional 11 megaparsecs away in 10 billion years then, obviously, it took the cluster the same length of time to reach its present distance from us. If we run time backwards we will find that 10 billion years ago the Virgo

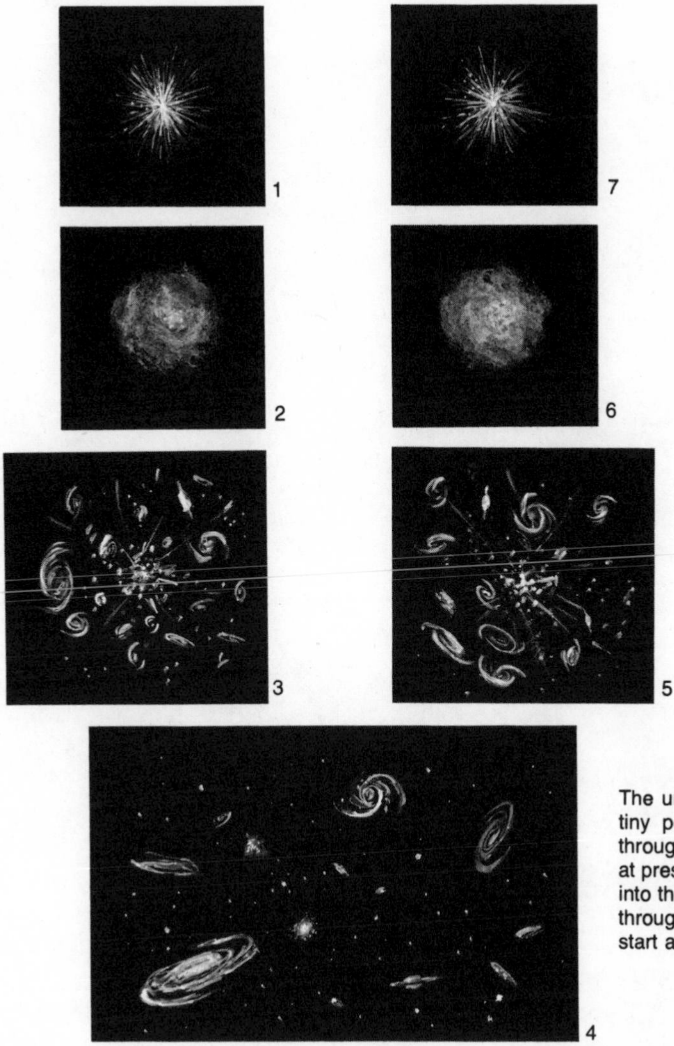


The universe may have evolved from a tiny point of pure energy (drawings 1 through 4). When it ceases expanding, as at present, it may begin to collapse back into the tiny point from which it began (5 through 7). Then the entire cycle might start again.

cluster was right on top of us. Similarly, if we run time backwards for any other galaxy or quasar we shall find that it too was right on top of us 10 billion years ago. If the universe expands as we go forward in time, it contracts as we look backward in time, so that it would have been crowded into a small space 10 billion years ago.

This central point would have been the beginning of everything—of the universe, of space, of time. Its exact determination

HALE OBSERVATORIES PHOTOGRAPH

Notice how the smaller of these two galaxies seems to be at the end of an arm of the other. A stream of stars connects them.

depends on an exact determination of the rate of expansion—the Hubble Constant. Using one estimate, we have found the age of the universe to be 10 billion years. Other, lower, figures for the Hubble Constant, based on a slower rate of expansion, give ages for the universe up to 20 billion years. We will, therefore, adopt an in-between figure, 15 billion years, as the age of the universe.

What we might call the creation would have been an explosion of all the matter in the universe in a space far too small to see. What we observe today, widely scattered galaxies slowing in their outbound race, is 15-billion-year-old fragments of that explosion, filling a sphere of space about 4,000 megaparsecs in diameter.

What came before? What will come after? If the universe keeps expanding, which is possible, the clusters of galaxies will eventually drift so far apart they will become almost invisible to one another and all the stars in all the galaxies we know will grow old and die and wink out one by one. (They could be replaced by new galaxies formed from new matter if the theories of astronomers Fred Hoyle and Thomas Gold are correct. In this case the universe would go on forever and would always look about the same. This theory is not accepted by most astronomers.) If the universe does not keep expanding, which is possible, then it will eventually begin to collapse and all the galaxies will return to the central point. There, the universe may just disappear, or it may start to expand again. Our universe may have been born after the collapse of an earlier one, and another may be born out of the collapse of ours, and so on, for endless generations of universes.

Whether the universe ends or not, we can be certain that our galaxy had a beginning. As we shall soon see, hydrogen is the fundamental fuel of the universe. If the galaxy were infinitely old, all its hydrogen would have been used up long ago. Unless hydrogen is still being created, as Mr. Hoyle has argued, this same argument indicates that the universe had a beginning. Whether the universe began or not, whether it will end or not, we do have some idea of how the sun and its planets came into being and gave rise to life. This is something we must understand if we are to speculate on the existence of SuperWorlds.

# 5: Stars: Births and Deaths

Hydrogen, the simplest and lightest element, is also the most abundant. Our planet Earth is, as we can see, a solid place, mostly made out of heavy elements. Indeed, it seems that iron, 56 times heavier than hydrogen, is the most plentiful element of the Earth. The sun, more than a million times as big as Earth, is only 333,000 times as massive. This is because it is composed of 99 percent of the two lightest elements. Three-quarters of the sun, or 75 percent, is hydrogen, and 24 percent is the second-lightest element, helium. Only 1 percent of the sun consists of the heavier elements, of which Earth and Earth's moon and the other three inner planets (Mercury, Venus, and Mars) are mostly composed.

All the other billions of blazing stars in the universe are also mostly hydrogen and helium. Iron and the other heavy elements are found only in small quantities. Besides, a great cloud of hydrogen fills our galaxy, and streams of the gas probably flow between galaxies in our cluster. The gas between the stars is thin, so thin that by earthly standards we speak of it as a vacuum; but in the 33 kiloparsec scale of the galaxy it amounts to a lot of hydrogen, very likely more hydrogen than composes all the stars.

Hydrogen is the basic element. The other elements are made out of the same things hydrogen is made of. Indeed, we can say that all elements are made out of hydrogen. Not only do we understand the ways in which hydrogen can be made into heavy elements, we have even turned it into a heavier element ourselves. We can turn hydrogen into the next heavier element, helium. This is the process known as fusion.

The building of heavy elements from hydrogen releases energy. This is the source of the energy of the sun, which is essentially a large fusion machine, turning about 1,500 million tons of hydrogen into 1,495.5 million tons of helium every second. The missing 4½ million tons becomes energy. To give some idea of the amount of energy this is, one *pound* of hydrogen represents the energy obtained by burning 290 million gallons of gasoline.

Fantastic as it seems, a cloud of hydrogen can become a galaxy of stars and planets, moons and comets, snails, blades of grass, and inquisitive minds. Each hydrogen atom has locked within it the secret of everything that has happened and is to be. As each of our cells bears within it the blueprint of a man, a hydrogen atom bears the blueprint of the universe.

Not that mankind has yet penetrated this secret. The early stages, particularly, remain mysterious, the picture becoming clearer as we approach the era of our sun. Our sun is only a third as old as the universe. Assuming that the explosion theory is correct, the universe was born 15 billion (75 galactic) years ago. We are quite certain that our sun and its family of planets were born about 25 galactic years ago and that life appeared here about 18 galactic years ago.

One of the mysteries is what happened to the antimatter.

Antimatter. Everything that is known of matter and its laws says that antimatter should exist. There should be equal amounts of matter and antimatter in the universe. The only trouble is, we can't find it.

Matter is energy. Energy is matter. We turn matter into energy all the time: burning wood, burning gasoline in our automobiles, splitting atoms in nuclear reactors.

"And the earth was without form, and void; and darkness was upon the face of the deep. And the spirit of God moved upon the face of the waters. And God said let there be light. . . ." The light was of the first stars, condensing out of galaxies that themselves may have condensed out of one great cloud. Each step brought more order into the universe—and each degree of order gave birth to a higher degree—ending with intelligence.

A burning log combines with oxygen from the air to make ashes and gases. Were we to weigh the log and the air before burning, and the ashes and gases afterwards, the ashes and gases would weigh less. This loss of weight, less than a billionth of an ounce, represents the tiny amount of mass that became heat and light as the log burned; just as 4½ million tons of the substance of the sun becomes the heat and light it broadcasts each second through the universe.

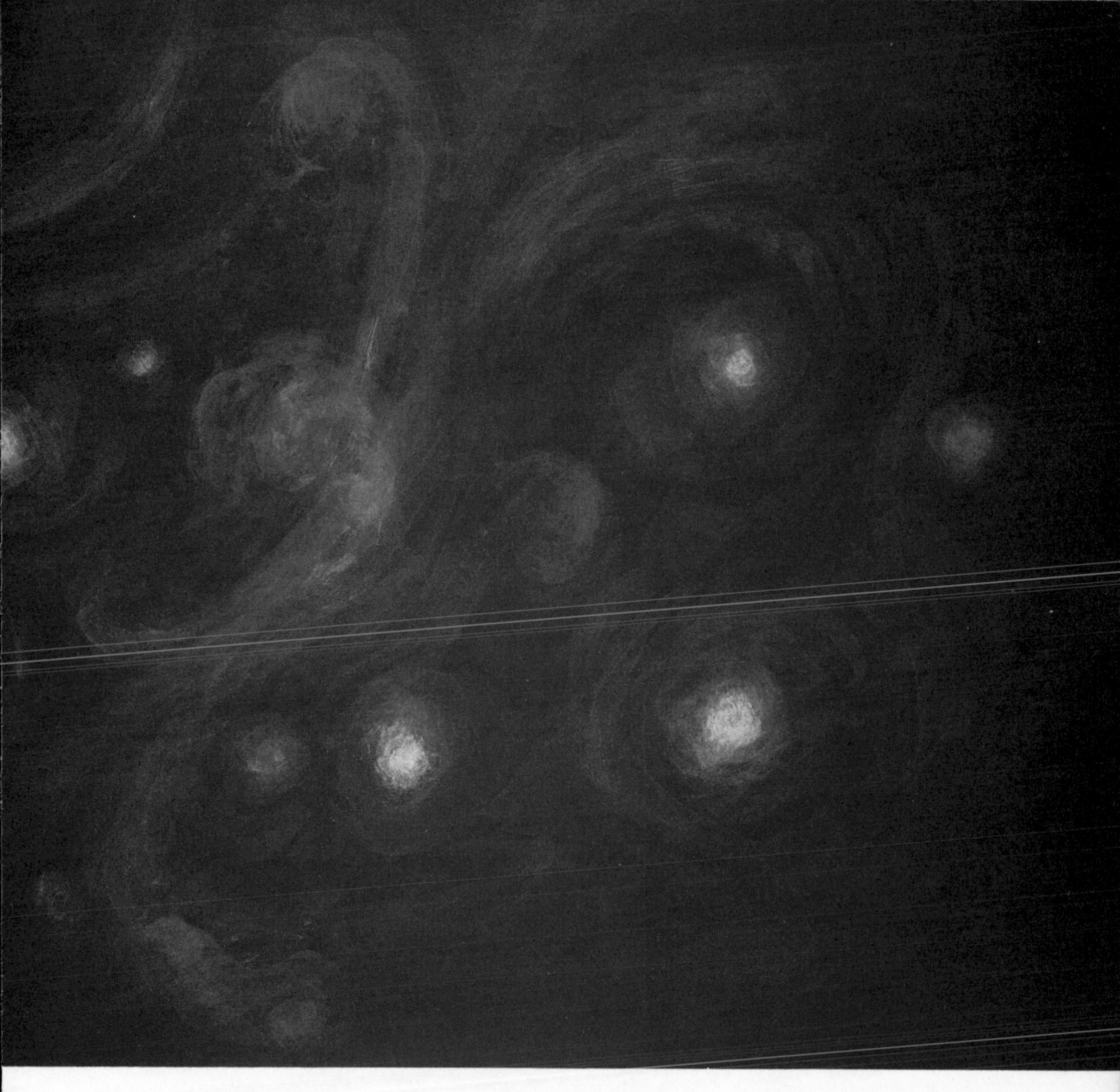

Energy is matter. We can reverse the process, building hydrogen out of energy. This is what may have happened in the first fraction of a second in the life of the universe. When we manufacture matter from energy in the laboratory, which we can do in very small amounts, we find that two kinds of matter are always equally produced: ordinary matter and antimatter.

To our eyes, antimatter would look just like matter. But if we happened to just touch a drop of, say, antimatter water, the result would be a violent explosion. When matter and antimatter meet, *all* the mass, not just 0.3 percent, as is the case with hydrogen fusion, is converted into energy.

One great puzzle is: if matter and antimatter were created in equal amounts at the birth of the universe, they would have destroyed themselves and become pure energy, and no matter would exist. Yet matter does exist, at least the ordinary kind of matter of which our planet and, as far as we know, the rest of our solar system is composed.

There are a number of possible explanations for the absence of antimatter:

- Matter was created by an unknown process.
- The two kinds of matter became separated at an early stage, in which case our own Milky Way galaxy consists of half one kind of matter and half the other; or it could be that entire galaxies are composed of one kind of matter or the other.

If antimatter does exist in our galaxy, there could be some unpleasant results someday, as envisaged in this poem about Dr. Edward Teller, an American physicist who supposed that antistars and even antigalaxies existed in other parts of the universe:

The Perils of Modern Living*
by Harold P. Furth

Well up beyond the tropostrata
There is a region stark and stellar
Where, on a streak of anti-matter,
Lived Dr. Edward Anti-Teller.

Remote from Fusion's origin,
He lived unguessed and unawares
With all his anti-kith and kin,
And kept macassars on his chairs.

One morning, idling by the sea,
He spied a tin of monstrous girth
That bore three letters: A.E.C.
Out stepped a visitor from Earth.

Then, shouting gladly o'er the sands,
Met two who in their alien ways
Were like as lentils. Their right hands
Clasped, and the rest was gamma rays.

In any case, explosive destruction of matter and antimatter could have provided energy needed to form the galaxies, two Swedish astronomers, Hannes Alfvén and Aina Elvius, believe.

Cells with enough mass to make a galaxy would have been formed by shock waves, the thunder of matter-antimatter explosions, and then gradually broken up into billions of separate smaller cells about a third of a parsec or less across, these smaller cells made of clumps of matter or of antimatter separated by magnetism and thereafter kept apart by sputtering explosions along their edges whenever clouds of the different kinds of matter touched.

Thickenings in the cells, caused by shock waves, were enough to start conditions in which gravity would take hold. Dense places in the cell exerted enough gravity to attract more gas in their direction, and the bigger they grew the more powerful their gravitational attraction became.

Slowly rotating, the great galactic clouds slowly contracted as matter concentrated toward their centers. At the same time, billions of the small cells also contracted, becoming hotter as they did so. The heat came from collisions of hydrogen atoms falling toward the centers of their cells. Slowed by bumping into other atoms, their speed was turned into heat.

If the cloud is big enough, its gravity will be strong enough to heat hydrogen at its center to the point where helium will be formed. This fusion reaction creates a lot more heat, and now an opposite reaction starts as the fusion heat pushes everything outward. If the cell has only about 1/30 as much matter as our sun, the fusion heat will push outward with such force that the cell will expand and cool to a point where the fusion reaction will stop. The cell, which lit up momentarily as the reaction started, will go dark. It may contract again after a while, and perhaps relight if it hasn't lost too much mass in the explosion. It may flicker on and off like this several times until it has lost so much matter that it can never light again.

A cell with mass amounting to about 1/25 that of our sun (about 40 times as big as our biggest planet, Jupiter) will stay lit once its fusion reaction starts, for its substance is such that the weight of hydrogen pressing in will prevent the hot center from expanding to the point where the fusion reaction stops. The outward push from the center will be balanced by the inward push of gravity, and the cell will keep fusing hydrogen in its center while maintaining its size. The interior fusion fire will radiate enormous amounts of energy at and near the wavelengths of visible light. The dark cell will have become a self-adjusting fusion machine. It will have become a star.

The kind of star it becomes depends on the size of the cloud out of which it contracted. The bigger the cell, the hotter and bigger its central fusion-furnace area, the hotter it will be at the surface, and the faster it will burn up all its hydrogen. Our sun, with only its central tenth fusing hydrogen, has been burning for 25 galactic years and may continue as it is for at least that many more. Remember, one galactic year is equal to 200 million Earth years. This means that 25 galactic years is the same as 5 billion Earth years. Stars 10 times as big can burn for no more than a million years, a mere galactic day and a half; stars three times as large as that burn out in a few galactic hours. (A galactic day is the equivalent of about 500,000 Earth years.)

Stars that burn hydrogen, as described above, are called Main Sequence stars. They have been classified according to their mass and surface temperatures. Their temperatures increase, and lifetimes shorten, with increasing mass. Our sun is a G 2 type star with a surface temperature of about 10,000 ° F (5,800 ° Kelvin. The Kelvin scale starts at absolute zero and uses centigrade degrees, which are 9/5ths as large as Fahrenheit degrees. The freezing point of water, for example, is 32 ° F, 0 ° Centigrade, and 273.16 ° Kelvin.)

Other Main Sequence stars are listed below; the unit for measuring mass and radius is the sun (sun mass = 1, sun radius = 1):

| Spectral Type | Mass | Radius | Surface Temp. in ° Kelvin | Number of Galactic Years Star Remains on Main Sequence |
|---|---|---|---|---|
| O 9.5 | 18 | 5.9 | 33,000 | |
| B 0 | 16 | 5.7 | 16,000 | 2 galactic weeks |
| B 9 | 2.9 | 2.5 | 10,800 | |
| A 0 | 2.6 | 2.3 | 9,500 | 2 |
| A 7 | 1.8 | 1.7 | 8,100 | |
| F 0 | 1.6 | 1.5 | 7,400 | 20 |
| F 8 | 1.2 | 1.1 | 6,100 | |
| G 0 | 1.08 | 1.05 | 5,900 | 55 |
| G 2 (sun) | 1 | 1 | 5,800 | 65 |
| G 8 | .85 | .87 | 5,300 | |
| K 0 | .83 | .83 | 5,100 | 140 |
| K 8 | .58 | .67 | 3,900 | |
| M 0 | .47 | .63 | 3,670 | |
| m 4 | .20 | .21 | 3,200 | 10,000 plus |

Of course a star can't keep turning hydrogen into helium forever. Eventually it will run out of hydrogen. The lifetimes of big stars on the Main Sequence, such as type B 0 and the 0's, are measured in galactic days or even hours. A medium-sized star like our sun will, after 50 or so galactic years on the Main Sequence, start expanding as the hydrogen in its core is used up. With nothing but helium left in the center, hydrogen fusion will continue in a shell around the center, the shell gradually moving toward the surface as the amount of helium increases. As this happens the sun will expand and get redder until it takes up all the space out to somewhere near the orbit of Earth.

Six billion years from now, our sun will begin swelling. It will become a red giant like Betelgeuse in the constellation Orion and destroy Earth's atmosphere and oceans. Before it is 9 billion years old it will explode and turn into a tiny white dwarf star.

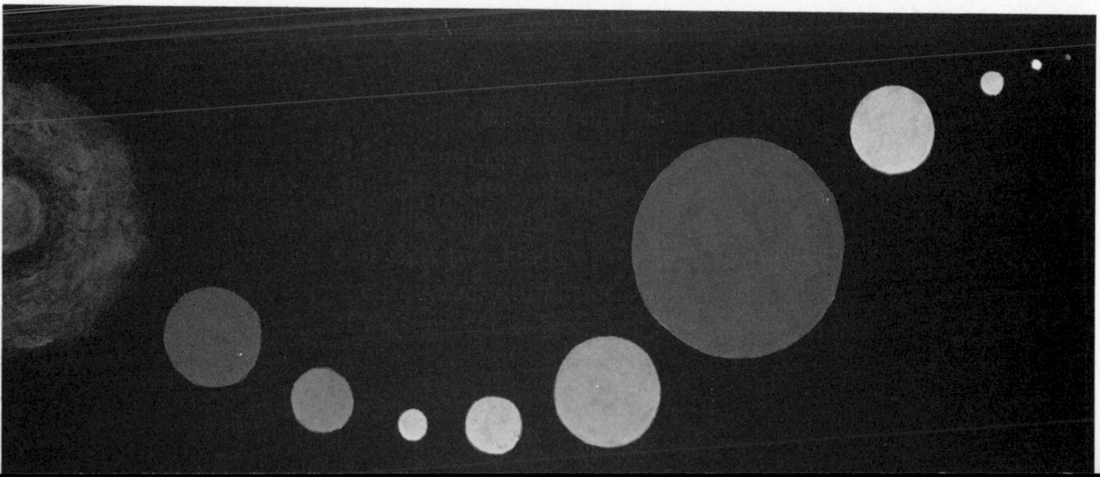

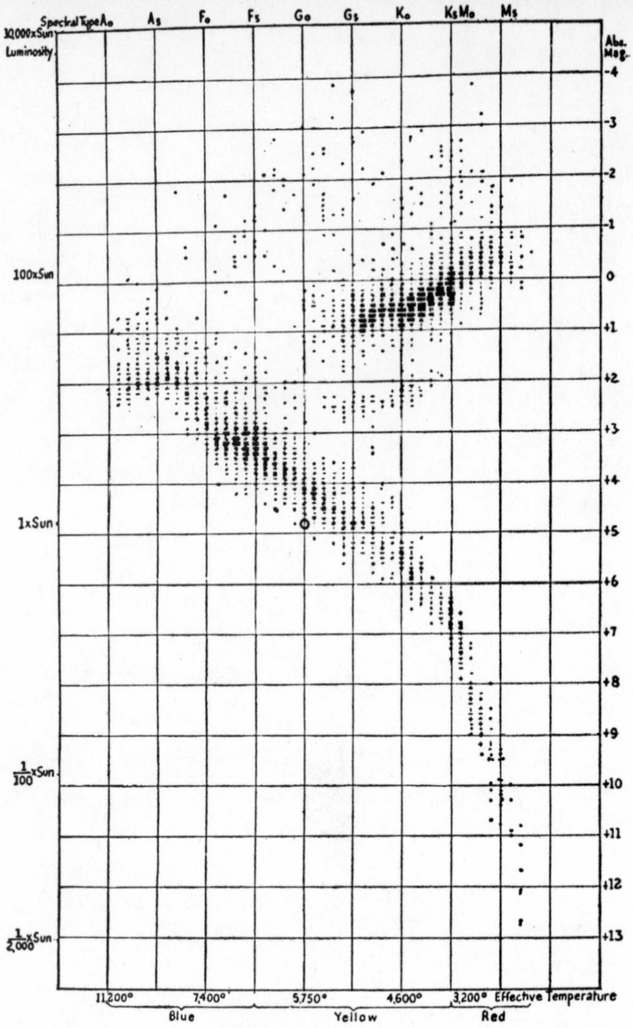


Each dot on this chart, prepared at Mount Wilson Observatory, represents a star. The horizontal scale shows the color, which indicates temperature from blue (11,200° K) at left to red (3,200° K) at right. The vertical scale shows brightness, from 1/2,000 th as bright as the sun to 10,000 times as bright.

As a red giant star, it will no longer be on the Main Sequence. Great hurricanes of turbulence will thrust large portions of the swollen star into space. Eventually it will collapse to a tenth or a hundredth of its former size, its surface white again and 10,000 ° K in temperature, but the total energy emitted will be a very small fraction of what it was during its Main Sequence lifetime. It will continue this way, a white dwarf, for many more galactic years, a feeble white ash in the darkness of space, composed of matter so compressed that a thimbleful will weigh several tons.

Stars more than 20 percent bigger than the sun (type F 8, and above, on the table on page 53), enter into a more violent history

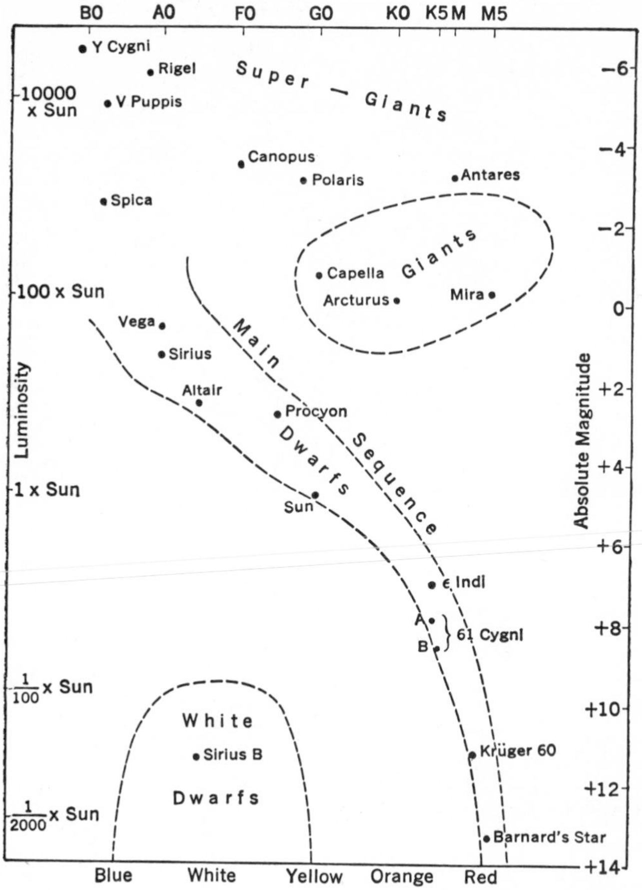


This chart is the same as the one on page 54, but with the names of certain stars shown. Note the position of our sun. All the stars in the Main Sequence are burning hydrogen, their differences in color and temperature depend basically on their size, with the smallest like Barnard's star, at the lower end. The giants, like Arcturus, have run out of hydrogen and are burning helium. The smaller stars, using up hydrogen more slowly, remain longer on the Main Sequence. Long after our sun has gone to join the giants 61 Cygni and E Indi will still be there.

as their central hydrogen is used up. They are able to compress the helium in their cores to the point where it starts fusing into even heavier elements. The temperature in the core of our sun, where hydrogen fusion takes place, is about 13.7 million degrees. At 100 million degrees, a temperature reached in the cores of stars 1.2 times the mass of the sun, helium turns into carbon and oxygen. At 600 million degrees, a temperature reached in even bigger stars, carbon turns into neon and magnesium and silicon. At 1,000 million degrees, silicon turns into iron. Sometimes these big stars explode, making even heavier elements during a brief period in which the star is as bright as a galaxy. This is called a Supernova.

HALE OBSERVATORIES PHOTOGRAPH

Probably the remains of a supernova. The outside of the star, now a giant shell of gas, will continue to race outward for millions of years, a source of the carbon, oxygen, iron, and other heavy elements that may one day form a flower or a leopard's fang.

What is left of the star after such an explosion? If its remaining mass is less than 40 percent more than the sun's mass, it will continue to contract until it reaches a diameter between 6 and 60 miles. As it contracts, the influences of gravity and pressure will cause all the electrons to collapse into the cores of their atoms, turning all the protons into neutrons. The star, in effect, will have become nothing but a mass of neutrons. Its rotational speed will have increased as it contracted until it is spinning at as much as 1,000 times a second. Its gravity will be so intense that anything that landed on it would be flattened and melted into neutrons.

HALE OBSERVATORIES PHOTOGRAPH

The remains of a supernova whose explosion lit up Earth's night sky 900 years ago. Chinese astronomers during the Sung dynasty recorded that it could be seen even during daylight.

Should the remaining mass be more than a few times the mass of our sun, the gravitational force would be powerful enough to overcome the force that maintains the shape of neutrons, and the star would continue to contract, growing smaller and smaller until it disappeared completely!

This is perhaps the strangest event in the universe. Gravity, like all other known physical forces, operates according to the inverse square principle. When two bodies move 100 times closer together, the gravitational attraction between them increases 10,000 times. As the star contracts, everything in it comes closer and closer together and the gravitational attraction becomes immensely more powerful. At a certain point it becomes so powerful that the speed of light, the speed limit of the universe, is less than the velocity needed to escape from the star's surface. (The escape velocity from Earth is 7 miles per second. An Apollo rocket must reach this speed in order to leave Earth. The star we are talking about becomes so dense that its escape velocity is more than 186,000 miles a second.)

Since light cannot leave the star, the star can no longer be seen by anyone outside the star. It has become what is known as a Black Hole. Some might escape this fate by blowing off enough mass in the course of an explosion to be left with less than the critical amount, one and a half or so solar masses; it seems likely however, that some big stars end up as Black Holes.

No one knows how many Black Holes there are in the sky. There have been speculations about them for more than forty years, but so far none have been certainly observed. A Black Hole would, of course, be difficult to see, since it would not give off any light and would absorb any light or other radiation that came its way. The only way to detect it would be as an invisible companion to another star. A Black Hole that had been a star in a double-star system would continue to revolve around its companion, whose motion would reflect its presence. One good possibility is Epsilon Aurigae, a fairly bright star that shines in front of the Milky Way, near Capella. Another is a star in Cygnus, a constellation that crosses the Milky Way near Vega.

Epsilon Aurigae is periodically eclipsed by an invisible com-

If we landed on this neutron star, the enormous gravity would squash us flatter than Saran wrap. The tiny pulsar at the heart of the Crab nebula rotates thirty times a second, broadcasting x-rays and other forms of radiation with an intensity equal to 10,000 suns like our own.

Cygnus X-1 and its blue companion might appear like this if Cygnus X-1 is indeed a Black Hole. Some scientists believe that the entire universe may eventually disappear into a Black Hole.

panion. Cygnus X-1 is an invisible x-ray star 2 kiloparsecs from Earth, whose companion is a blue supergiant. Cygnus X-1 seems to be sucking chunks of matter away from its giant companion.

If all big stars become Black Holes, it is possible that at least a great deal of all the matter in the universe is now in this form. And since Black Holes keep attracting matter to them, they keep growing. It is even possible that there are entire black galaxies in which matter has been absorbed by their Black Holes.

It is also possible that some rather large Black Holes exist in the core of our galaxy, the remains of giant stars that formed in that region of concentrated matter. One possible explanation for mysterious forces emanating from there is that these holes are devouring stars at the rate of fifty or more a year.

Black Holes may be even more common. It is possible for any amount of matter in excess of about 1/100,000th of a gram to become a Black Hole if it is compressed enough. Our sun, for example, would become a Black Hole if its diameter were reduced to less than 3.6 miles. Earth would become a Black Hole if it shrunk to a diameter a bit less than 1 inch. Tiny Black Holes could have been created by the shock waves at the time the universe began. They would have flown through space until drawn to the heart of some shining star, whose substance they would then begin to devour from within.

Black Holes have some very peculiar properties. Later on we will discuss how they might assist us in our search for SuperWorlds, and even lead to the ultimate adventure.

HALE OBSERVATORIES PHOTOGRAPH

Globular star cluster.

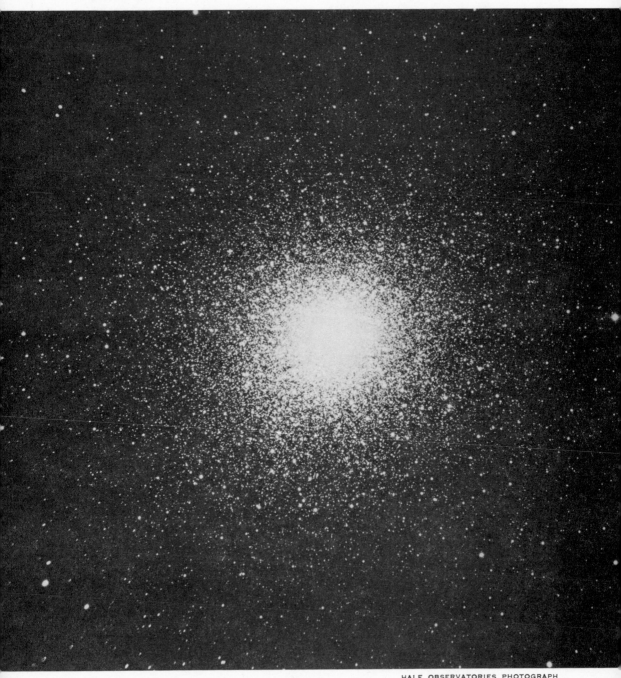

# 6: Planets: Dust to Dust

Reviewing this life story of the stars, we can see that hydrogen by itself can collapse into a star that, if it is big enough, can manufacture all the heavy elements either in its core or by explosion. Since our sun is too small to manufacture elements heavier than helium, the 1 percent of such elements in its substance must have been made in other stars. The cell from which it contracted must have contained, in addition to the primordial hydrogen, material spewed out of some dying giant star.

We can see this happening: the original galactic cloud expanding, billions of cells collapsing into stars; the larger stars exploding quickly, seeding space with heavy elements to be incorporated into succeeding generations of stars like our sun.

At least 90 percent of the stars in our galaxy appear to be of older generations, since they contain much smaller proportion of heavy elements, as little as 1/100th as much as our sun. These older stars, called Population II stars, are found everywhere in the galaxy. All the stars above and below the spiral arms in the central disk are Population II, as are those in the great sphere at the galaxy's core.

Many of these Population II stars are found in globular clusters, balls composed of tens of thousands of stars in constant rapid motion, like swarms of bees. These clusters are scattered through the cloudy mist of stars that envelopes the galaxy. When the stars in the clusters are analyzed, it is found that they contain none of the heavier Main Sequence stars. Since the heavier stars have the shortest lifetimes, this indicates that the age of the clusters is such that by now all the heavier stars have used up their hydrogen and left the Main Sequence to become giants, dwarfs, neutron stars, or Black Holes. This means that Population II stars are older than stars like our sun. It is thought that they were born 50 or more galactic years ago, when the galaxy was still a great sphere of gas, before the increasing speed of rotation caused it to flatten into its present lens shape.

The small picture at top, center, shows the locations of (A) and (B), parts of the Andromeda system. (A) shows a spiral arm region of young Population I stars like our sun. (B) is a small companion galaxy of Population II stars. HALE OBSERVATORIES PHOTOGRAPH

Those Population II stars that are not in clusters buzz around the galaxy in all different directions. Long after their birth, the disk was formed with its stars wheeling around the center. Stars like the sun, with many times the amounts of heavy elements of Population II stars, are called Population I stars. Population I stars are found only in the spiral arms. Many Population II stars have wandered into the spiral arms, where they can be picked out by their random motions.

This difference between the two populations of stars will take on importance when we begin to consider the likelihood that there are planets like Earth circling other stars. For if, as seems likely, stars and their planets are born out of the same clouds of material, it would seem that the stuff of which many of the older Population II stars are made could not form an Earth. We will return to this later.

The birth of Population I stars may be different from that of the older stars. We have seen that there is lots of dust in the spiral arms, dust that hides from our view the galactic core in Sagittarius. No one knows how this dust comes to be in space. It consists of tiny particles of sand, compounds of carbon, and graphite.

The difficulty with stars forming after a galaxy's first 25 galactic years of life is that all the existing myriads of stars pour out enough energy to heat up cells of gas to the extent that it would be impossible for them to condense into stars.

The dust enables new stars to incubate. It works in several ways. First, by screening out starlight—energy—it makes cold spaces. The temperature throughout the galaxy is about 90 ° Kelvin (− 183 ° Centigrade). Inside the dust clouds, the temperature goes down to 5 ° Kelvin. At this temperature, hydrogen turns into ice, collecting around the particles of dust within the cloud. In this dark region, snowstorms about a parsec across develop. As the snowflakes swirl they cling together, and a slow process of accretion —of building up clumps of ice of larger and larger sizes—begins. Meanwhile, the shielding dust helps in another way. The light from surrounding stars strikes it but does not penetrate. Coming from all sides, it exerts pressure on the outside of the cloud, compressing its contents and assisting the concentration taking place inside.

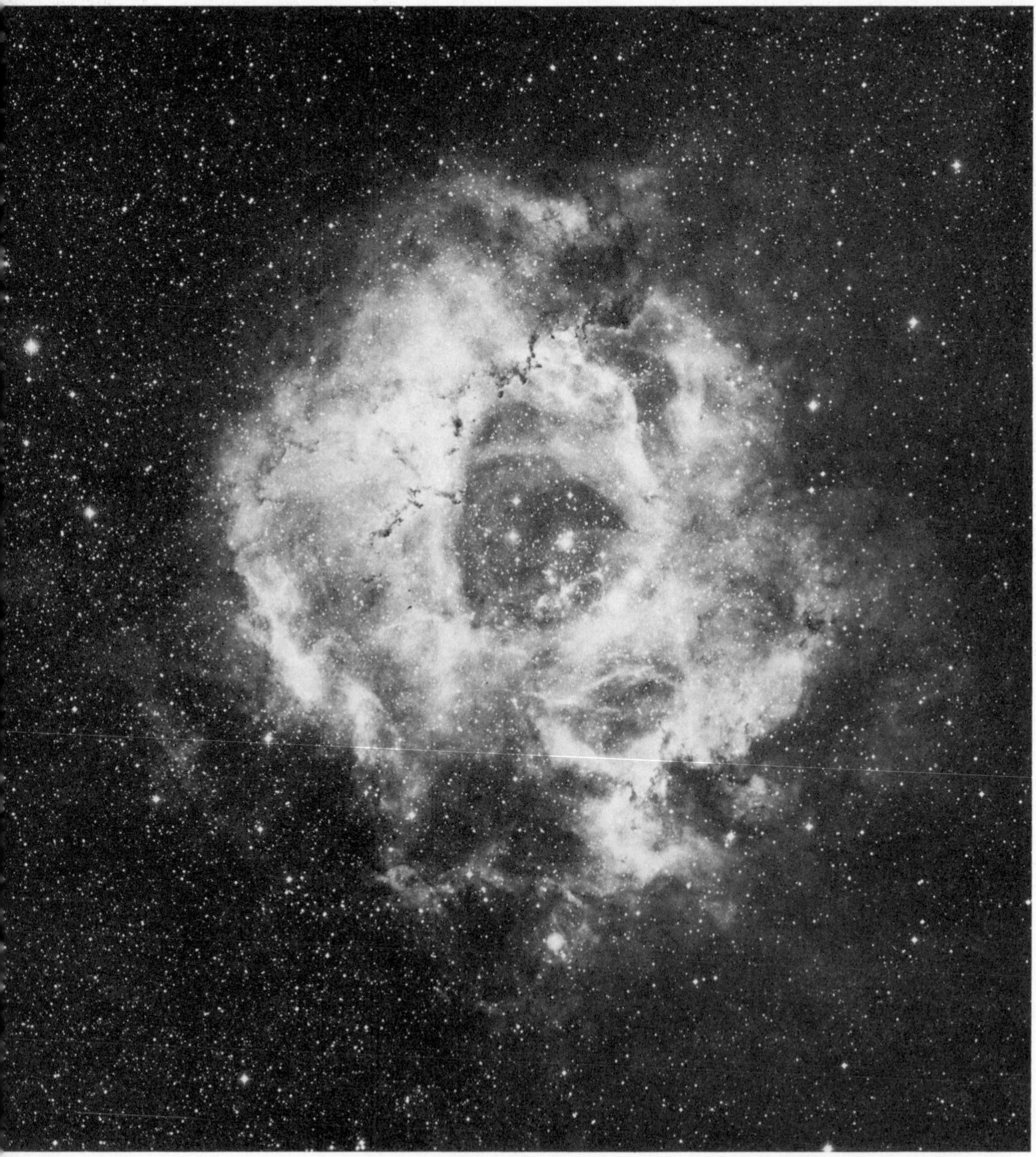

A

HALE OBSERVATORIES PHOTOGRAPH

B

HALE OBSERVATORIES PHOTOGRAPH

The dark spots are great dust clouds, frigid regions where stars are being born. (B) is an enlargement of a portion of (A). Carbon is needed in the birth of stars at this stage in the universe's development. It makes the dust particles sticky, helping them to grow.

The cloud also removes heat from the condensing mass while keeping heat from other sources away. Thus the mass of hydrogen snow can keep contracting without heating up to a point where the stuff would boil away, stopping the process of contraction. It is able to contract until a fusion fire lights up within its depths. Now the heat and radiation push away the dust, revealing a new star.

While the seething snowstorm collapsed into a star, something else was happening. As the great dirty snowball collapsed, rotating faster, a flat disk formed around the equator of the central ball. Snowy dust in the disk stuck together, and globules started to grow, attracting more slush particles by gravity. In this way, planets grow around a star as the star itself is born.

If all the rotational energy of the original snowstorm had ended up in the sun, collapsed to less than 1/20,000,000th the size of the original storm, the sun would spin at a rate of more than 100 miles per second at its equator. It spins much more slowly, at only about 1 mile per second, because most of the original rotation (angular momentum) has ended up in the planets.

When the rotational speed of stars is measured, it is found that they fall into two distinct groups. Medium-sized stars, like our sun, and smaller stars spin slowly. All stars that are at least a third bigger than our sun spin swiftly. Since our sun's slow spin rate is explained by its having given most of its original spin to its family of planets, it seems likely that all slow-spinning stars have planets.

The evolution of the solar system. Even as the planets and comets were forming, so were complicated chemicals based on carbon, early steps on the road to life.

The reason why bigger stars do not have planets may be that their greater heat blows globules apart before they can clump into planets.

Now we are ready to make some guesses about the number of stars in our galaxy that have planets. First of all, we can eliminate stars that are not on the Main Sequence, for in their giant phases they would have gobbled up any planets they had that were close enough to be Earthlike. That leaves 98 percent of the stars. Of these, 7 percent are big, fast-spinning stars, so we can eliminate them. We must also eliminate stars inside the central core of the galaxy, where they are too close together to permit planets to stay in orbits. We must also eliminate about half of all the rest of the stars, which are parts of two-star systems (and even of systems with three or more stars). We just don't know enough to guess at how the presence of a second star within AU's of another, would affect the chances of life, and intelligence, evolving on a planet of one of the stars. This leaves about 40 percent of all the stars in the galaxy as possible homes of planets.

The surface of Mars shows evidence of liquid water. We shall soon know if there is life here, or elsewhere in our system.

Does that star at the left end of the constellation Casseopia have any planets? If so, are any of them inhabited by living things? That star is our sun, as seen from a planet of Alpha Centauri.

We aren't interested in just planets, however. We are interested in Earthlike planets that could be sites of SuperWorlds.

There would not be enough heavy elements available around an older, Population II, star to make a planet like ours. At least 90 percent of all the stars in our galaxy are members of Population II. Actually, there are many generations of stars of all ages between the oldest of Population II and Population I stars like our sun, and

with gradually increasing abundance of heavy elements; and there are stars younger than our sun, as well as stars being born today. If, conservatively, we eliminate all stars of generations older than the sun, we are left with about 10 billion possible sites of Earthlike planets in the galaxy, all in the disk among the spiral arms. There may also be strewn through the galaxy hundreds of millions of dark bodies, concretions of matter too small to have ever burned as stars. It is estimated that there are six such planetlike objects, ranging in size from that of Mars to double the size of Jupiter, in every cubic parsec. The Harvard astronomer Harlow Shapley thought that some of these sunless planets may, by radioactive processes like those that cause Earth's volcanoes, generate enough heat of their own to support life.

Looking up into the night sky we are looking at hundreds of other suns. Some, like Altair in the constellation Eagle, are too hot to have planets. Others, like Procyon in the Little Dog have companion stars. Planets are so small and dark that we cannot see them from here, even circling the nearest stars. The astronomer Peter Van de Kamp has detected the planet of another star by the way that star's path wobbles, pulled from side to side by an invisible planet(s) as it moves through space. This sun, Barnard's star, is the nearest known single star. It is only 2 parsecs distant.

Of the forty-one stars nearest the sun, five, including Barnard's, seem to have invisible companions of planetary size (less than 1/20th the mass of the sun):

| Star | Approximate Size of Companion (Jupiter, 1/1000th Mass of Sun = 1) | Spectral Type | Distance in Parsecs | |
|---|---|---|---|---|
| Barnard's | 1.5 | M 5 | 2 | |
| Lalande 21185 | 10 | M 2 | 2.5 | |
| 61 Cygni A | 8 | K 6 | 3.4 | double star |
| Krueger 60A | 9 to 25 | M 4 | 4 | double star |
| Bd $-20°$ 2465 | 20 | M 4 | 4.7 | |

It is possible that the motions now attributed to one large planet are caused by several smaller ones.

Many of the planets of other suns are doubtless as dead as our moon. Is there at least one life-bearing planet in each solar system? Is there on each life-bearing planet some form of intelligent life? What are the chances that this intelligent life equals or surpasses our achievements? These are the next questions we must examine in our search for SuperWorlds.

# 7: Life: Order Out of Chaos

In the one solar system we know something about, life has evolved on at least one of nine planets.

How did life evolve on Earth?

All living things we know of are made almost entirely of four chemical elements: hydrogen, oxygen, carbon, and nitrogen. Hydrogen, of course, is the most common element in the universe, and the other three are plentiful since they can be made in stars that are only 20 percent bigger than the sun.

Radio telescopes have found these elements of life everywhere in the galaxy, even combined into compounds that once were thought to be formed only in living things. Formaldehyde, a precurser of sugar, has been detected in two galaxies outside our own, which indicates that the ingredients for life are probably common throughout the universe. In our own galaxy twenty-three different organic molecules—stepping stones to life—have been found in the spaces between the stars.

Exactly how living matter arises out of these compounds is not clearly understood; a rough outline of the process can be perceived.

Our sun is about 25 galactic years (5 billion Earth years) old.

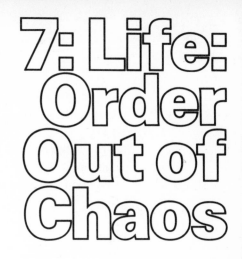

The oldest rocks on Earth are about 22½ galactic years old. It is believed that in the beginning the atmosphere of Earth was like the present atmospheres of Jupiter and Saturn, that is, composed of the six most abundant elements: hydrogen, helium, oxygen, carbon, neon, and nitrogen. Much of these were combined in the form of ammonia (nitrogen and hydrogen), methane (carbon and hydrogen), and water (hydrogen and oxygen). Also present were formaldehyde and other complicated compounds.

The basic building blocks of living matter are amino acids, sugars, certain other acids, and purines and pyramidines. It has been shown in the laboratory that amino acids, sugars, and quite complicated component parts of the other substances are produced when electric sparks, or ultraviolet radiation, are passed through a mixture of gases like that which made up Earth's early atmosphere. Indeed, it is even possible that these compounds were formed along with Earth and its sun, since some of them have been detected in the dust clouds among the stars. Amino acids combine in chains to become proteins. Purines and pyramidines combine with certain sugars and acids to make RNA and DNA. Proteins are the stuff of life—of muscle, skin, and nerve. RNA and DNA are the organizing principle of life.

Lightning in the atmosphere added to the supply of amino acids, sugars, parts of purines and pyramidines, and other acids and ingredients, the stuff raining down on the primitive oceans and land. For many millions of Earth years it rained, making a soup in the surface of the restless sea and dripping and sizzling on rocks and new-formed lava. Just as hydrogen and oxygen naturally combine to form water, amino acids combined into chains; and sugars mixed with things like purines, all in millions of different combinations.

Order was coming into the world. It was as if the things in the broth were becoming parts of a giant jigsaw puzzle, billions of jigsaw pieces in motion as the sun moved around the galaxy. When, somehow, they fell into the right place, the pictures they formed would be proteins and something else (DNA) that could make copies of proteins out of amino acids. Finally, there was a cell moving through the broth in search of the amino acid food it needed to make copies of itself.

Now that the building blocks of proteins and DNA have been detected in the spaces between the stars, we cannot rule out the possibility that it has evolved in space.

Order is the fundamental characteristic of life. Everything else in the universe proceeds in the direction of disorder. A star cooks a broth of heavy elements and spews it into space. The star becomes dust. Galaxies break apart, heat and light—EM radiation—stream through the vastness of space never to be recovered (unless the universe collapses). Stars run down. Only life runs up, building order out of chaos. It preserves complicated genetic messages over millions of years, building human beings, snails, and flowers out of water, air, and dirt.

Life arises on a voyage through space and time. We must follow our sun as it floats outward in the gas and dust of the spiral

The amoeba is a very complicated organism. It probably took life as long to evolve from its first simple viruslike molecules to the amoeba as it took to get from the amoeba to robins, moths, and men.

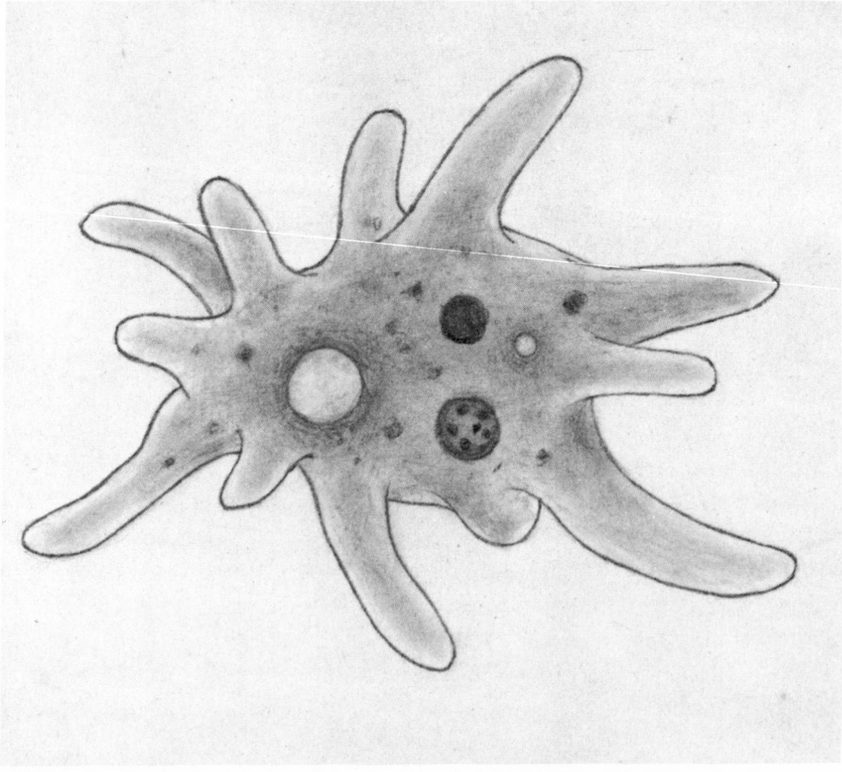

arm and makes its 200-million-year circuits of the galactic core. We will use the galactic year, equal to 200 million of our years, in following the progress of life. It was some 4.5 billion Earth years, 23 galactic years, ago, that our planet assumed a recognizable form. As it follows the sun around the galaxy it is probably exposed, once every three or four galactic years, to the intense radiation of a nearby supernova. Five galactic years after the Earth's beginning, 18 galactic years ago, the first cell was born. At first this cell fed on the stuff in the primeval broth. The supply ran low as the seas filled with cells. Then some cells found a way of making food out of water and carbon dioxide, using the energy of the sun.

This is called photosynthesis. It is the process by which green plants exist. The green is the green of chlorophyll, the protein that does the manufacturing. A by-product of photosynthesis is oxygen. The living plants in the ocean gradually changed Earth's atmosphere, enriching it with free oxygen. Other creatures developed ways of using the free oxygen to burn the living matter of plants, and so there were two kinds of life: plants using the energy of sunlight, and animals using the energy of plants and of the oxygen made by plants.

After the passage of galactic years, mountains formed, and continents. Continents drifted apart through the waters, living things changed and evolved, new creatures appeared, old ones died out: jellyfish, worms, sponges, crabs, clams, fish. Plants found ways of surviving out of the sea, and animals followed them onto the land, from beaches, rivers, and swamps to soggy bottom lands, up soggy slopes to the drier plains.

Let us say that life appeared 5 galactic years after the Earth was formed. In another 15 galactic years, the seas were full of fish. Eight months later plants were growing on land. Two months later vertebrates (animals with backbones) and invertebrates (animals without backbones) followed the plants ashore. Six weeks later life was becoming more independent of water. Reptiles, the first animals that could reproduce without laying their eggs in water, and seed ferns, the first plants whose lives could develop outside of water, appeared. Nine months later, came the dinosaurs and insects with wings, and 8 months after that, the first mammals and

Man appeared about 2 million years ago, out of the primates, of the mammals, of the amphibians, of the bony fishes, of the. . . . Each creature we see today, sand crab, tree, toad, or tuna, has as long and distinguished a history.

birds. This was 21 galactic years and 8 months since the Earth was formed, 16 years and 8 months since the first cell. At 21 years 11 months, the dinosaurs died out and flowering plants appeared. At 22 years and 2 galactic months, mammals were taking over the land. A little less than 2 months later, many mammals that we would recognize today appeared. Five galactic weeks later, apes spread over the African plains, and 6 months and 3 weeks after that, the first men could be seen. It took 22 years and 49 weeks, galactic time, for men to arrive on the scene. A few galactic days later (about 2 million Earth years) they had walked on the moon and built radio telescopes to tune in on the galaxy.

The time needed to go from planet formation to technology is about 23 galactic years (4.5 billion years); from primitive cell to technology, 18 galactic years (3.5 billion years).

We would not expect, then, to find a SuperWorld capable of sending a space probe our way as the companion of a star that had been burning for less than 23 galactic years (4.5 billion Earth years). Guessing that life developed on Earth at the earliest possible moment, we would expect that SuperWorlds would have suns as old as ours, or older.

# 8: Other Worlds

We can only guess at how many of these older suns possess a life-bearing planet. Such a planet would have to meet certain requirements. It would have to be the right distance from its sun to have liquid water. It would have to be big enough to have sufficient gravity to keep its atmosphere from flying off into space—at least .4 as massive as Earth (Mars is only .13 as massive). It must rotate on its axis so that it has days and nights to smooth out temperature variation, and the axis of rotation must be fairly upright with respect to its sun. The day-night requirement causes a problem for planets of small stars. The smaller the star, the closer to it the planet must be to get sufficient heat; but if a planet gets too close to its sun, tidal forces slow its rotation almost to a stop. Mercury, for example, the planet nearest our sun, has only three of its days in two of its years. A planet with that slow a rotation would always have one side too hot to support life. A planet with an axis of rotation pointing toward or near its sun would have very extreme seasonal changes, going from very hot to very cold, with moderate temperatures only along a narrow band near its equator. In our solar system, one planet, Uranus, is in this condition.

Since we do not know the laws, if any, governing the sizes of planets, their distances from their star, and so on, we have no way of knowing how likely it is that any solar system will have at least one inhabited planet. Some have speculated that all solar systems would be very much alike, on the theory that they are giant crystals (on Earth we find that quartz, salt, sugar, and other substances always form crystals of the same shape). Others have supposed that each solar system would be different.

Using what we know of our own solar system as a rough guide, Dr. Stephen H. Dole of the Rand Corporation estimated the chances of life-bearing planets being found with different types of stars. Confining himself to slow-revolving stars on the Main Sequence, from type F 2, about a third more massive than the sun, to type K 1, about two thirds the mass of the sun, he found the probabilities small at these two extremes and increasing as one approached the middle range of G type stars, close in size to our sun. The chance of a star like our sun having an inhabited planet, he said, was 1 out of 18. At the extremes, the chance of finding such a planet near a big F 2 star was 1 out of 94; and near a small K 1, 1 out of 164. The average chance for the existence of an inhabited planet around any of the stars in this range was 1 out of 27.

Using these figures, we can make some guesses as to the number of life-bearing planets in our galaxy. The stars we know most about are those closest to us. We will make a census of the fifty-five closest known stars to a distance of 5.1 parsecs. The first thing we find is that thirty-six of them, almost three fourths, must be eliminated from consideration as too small, all M type stars, smaller than the Ks, which, Dole found, were the smallest that could be expected to have habitable planets. Many of these M stars are also members of multiple-star systems, which, we feel, would also eliminate them from consideration.

Eliminating all stars in multiple systems, whatever their type,

It would be difficult for planets of stars in double systems to have orbits stable enough to nurture life.

subtracts another twelve, leaving us with eight possibilities. In addition to our sun, these are:

| Name | Type | Distance in Parsecs |
|---|---|---|
| Epsilon Eridani | K 2 | 3.3 |
| Epsilon Indi | K 5 | 3.5 |
| Tau Ceti | G 4 | 3.6 |
| van Maanen's star | white dwarf | 4.3 |
| Groombridge 1618 | K 5 | 4.5 |
| CC 658 | white dwarf | 4.9 |
| Altair | A 5 | 5 |

Of these, all must be eliminated save one. The white dwarfs are no longer on the Main Sequence; the K 2 and K 5s are too small, Altair, the A 5, is too big. Not only does it spin swiftly, indicating an absence of planets, but its Main Sequence lifetime is too short. This leaves only Tau Ceti, among our fifty-five nearest neighbors, as a possible home of life.

Tau Ceti is an ordinary looking star, seen in the autumn sky to the west of Orion, about equal in brightness to the star that marks the place where the handle joins the Big Dipper.

Tau Ceti is a G 4 type star, slightly smaller than our sun, but of the group to which Dole assigns the greatest chance of having habitable planets, 1 in 18. One out of 55 stars has 1 out of 18 chances of having a life-bearing planet. This means that the chance of any one of these nearest stars having such a planet is 1 out of 990, say 1 in 1,000.

These nearest stars, all neighbors in our spiral arm, are members of Population I. We have already decided that Population I stars, comprising about one tenth of the stars in the galaxy, are the most probable homes of Earthlike planets and life. Rounding off our estimate of the chances of any of the nearest, best-known Population I stars of having a life-bearing planet to 1 out of 1,000, we can apply that to the number of Population I stars in the galaxy to get an estimate of the number of life-bearing planets.

There are 250 billion stars in the galaxy. Of these, 10 percent, or 25 billion, are members of Population I. Of these, 1 out of 1,000 has a life bearing planet; 1/1000th of 25 billion is 25 million.

Twenty-five million life-bearing planets in the galaxy.

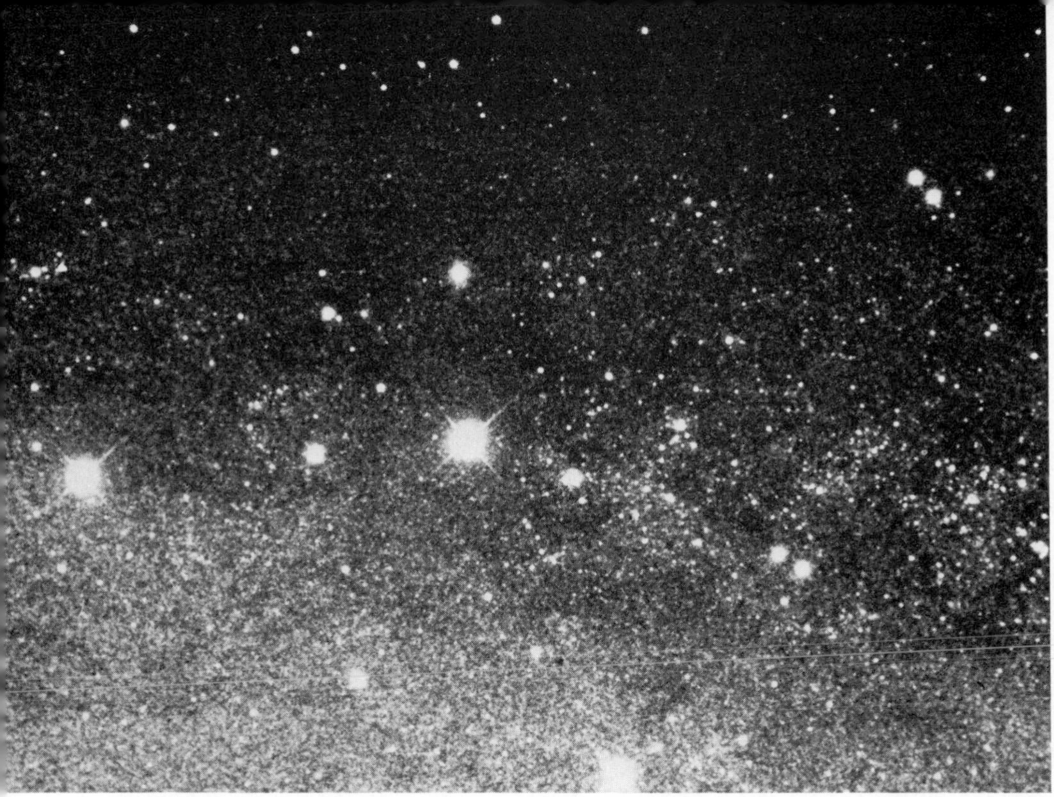

HALE OBSERVATORIES PHOTOGRAPH

Population II stars near the center of the galaxy in Andromeda.

HALE OBSERVATORIES PHOTOGRAPH

If our galaxy has 25 million life-bearing planets, there ought to be an equal number here, in our twin galaxy in Andromeda.

HALE OBSERVATORIES PHOTOGRAPH

A galaxy in the constellation Virgo. SuperWorlds could have flourished and disappeared in the 40 million years it has taken light from this galaxy to reach us.

# 9: Intelligence at Large

We are now ready to guess about the prevalance of SuperWorlds.

Assuming stars have been, and are being, born at a steady rate throughout the history of the galaxy, or at least of the disk, and our star is about half as old as the galaxy, then half the stars in the disk are older than the sun.

Assuming also that Earth is average, we would not expect technology to develop on other worlds in less time than it took to develop on Earth. SuperWorlds, therefore, would have to be at least as old as Earth.

Half of 25 million is 12½ million. Are all of these SuperWorlds? What if their superior civilizations have disappeared? How long does a technological civilization last?

If we define a technological civilization as one that can be detected over stellar distances, then we have been a technological civilization for about fifty years. It is our broadcasting of radio waves that first made us detectable to others, and the big radio telescopes of the late 1950s that first gave us the ability to detect other inhabited planets.

This ability has been achieved along with the ability to destroy ourselves, either by nuclear explosions or destruction of our planet's ecosystem. These achievements must always be linked. Understanding of EM radiation, the basis of radio, leads to knowledge of the structure of atoms.

If a technological civilization survives, on the average, only one hundred years, then the number of such civilizations in the galaxy at any one time would be greatly reduced. If 25 galactic years (5 billion Earth years) remain before our sun leaves the Main Sequence, then we can say this is the theoretical maximum life for a technological civilization on Earth. If it lasts 100 years, it exists only for 1/50,000,000 of this time, 15 galactic seconds.

If technological civilizations last a mere fraction of a galactic minute, there could be only one in the entire galaxy at any one time. Assuming that more than one technological civilization could evolve on a planet, as others might, in the future, evolve on Earth out of rats, lemurs, frogs, or squids, the number could be doubled or tripled, still leaving the galaxy a lonely place for the mind.

It has been as difficult to estimate the life-span of civilizations as it has been to estimate any of the other possibilities of planets and life. Among those who have considered this problem, there seems to be general agreement that the first few hundred years are the most dangerous, that if a technological civilization can learn to control its nuclear weapons and population growth, and to manage its ecosystem, it could be around for a long time. Even if it survives, however, there is a chance that a technological civilization would lose its interest in technology, turning inward in philosophical contemplation or backsliding in physical and mental decay.

Should technological civilizations last a thousand Earth years, there could be 2 or 3 in the galaxy at one time. A 10,000 year lifetime would give us about 25 in the galaxy; lifetimes of 100,000 Earth years, 250; of a million years, 2,500.

Of course the number of existing civilizations is not the same as the number of SuperWorlds. Any one civilization, if it survived, would reach a stage where it would colonize the planets of other stars. This increases the number of SuperWorlds, and also the chances of survival over time.

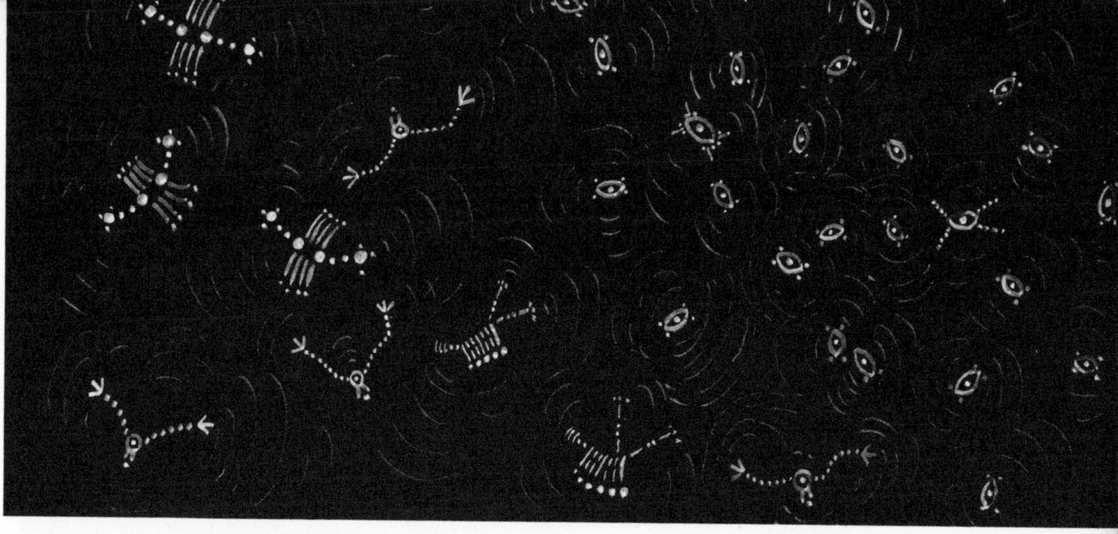

If we were to meet with a civilized insect swarm on some other planet, neither of us might be aware of the other's intelligence.

Another possibility is that we are at the threshhold of a new and final stage of evolution, the creation of artificial intelligence. Computers capable of reproducing and improving themselves could survive destruction of the ecosystem since they are not biological. Powered directly by the sun or other energy sources, and with electronic circuits that perform best in a vacuum, artificial intelligences may prove to be the ultimate form of "life." This will be discussed at greater length in chapter 11.

Study of evolution as it has taken place on Earth has led to different conclusions about the appearance of other intelligent beings. The paleontologist George Gaylord Simpson, of Harvard, doubts that they would resemble humans on the grounds that most evolutionary paths are dead ends and the continuance of certain lines is largely a matter of chance.

Looking back over the long record of earthly evolution, it can be seen that most creatures became extinct without leaving descendants. Only a small proportion of all the possible animals that could have evolved has evolved. Whether man would have evolved or not, in Simpson's view, could depend on whether or not a certain fish, 300-million Earth years ago, swam north or south. Also, in Simpson's view, one cannot argue from the fact that humans do exist that a similar creature would have evolved in any event to fill the place of man in the scheme of nature. All possible places in nature are not filled.

The dolphin and some of the whales may be more intelligent than we are. So far, none of us has figured out a way of communicating. The task of communicating with SuperWorlds may even be more difficult than we think.

Other students of evolution take a different approach, pointing out that many animals have evolved along separate lines to arrive at similar shapes and roles. Conical shells, for example, have been evolved separately by four entirely different kinds of animals at four widely spaced times, the earliest by a member of the jellyfishes, more than 300 million years ago, the most recent by an arthropod, about 8 million years ago. Arthropods, which include insects, spiders, and crabs, are as different from jellyfish as mammals.

Other, even more striking, examples of convergence are the similar shapes of the shark (a primitive fish), the icthyosaur (a now extinct reptile), and the dolphin (a mammal); also the Tasmanian wolf, an Australian marsupial that looked and acted like the wolves that evolved in other parts of the world from the carnivore family; and the Meadowlark and the Longclaw. The Meadowlark, a member of the blackbird family, evolved in America; the Longclaw, a member of the pipit family, in Africa. They are so much alike in shape, colors, habits, and song that only an expert can tell them apart.

Identical needs seem to produce identical, or near identical, organs. The line of descent leading to the squid, an invertebrate, separated from that leading to man, a vertebrate, over 420 million earth years ago. With a common ancestor whose eye could have been nothing more than a spot of pigment, squid and man independently evolved eyes with adjustable lenses, irises, and retinas that work almost exactly the same. It does not seem far-fetched to suppose, then, that on any life-bearing planet with a fair amount of land, intelligent creatures with hands and eyes will evolve.

The creatures of other worlds may be neither animals nor plants. They may also be immature stages that become transformed, as caterpillars become butterflies. They may even be sophisticated machines. We shall look as queer to them as they do to us.

Upright posture also seems necessary for the development of technical intelligence, since this frees the hands for tool using. Handless intelligence, as in the dolphin or whale, might be high, but would not result in a technological civilization.

Since we have plenty of examples of evolution following similar paths on Earth, and we know that advantageous changes have also happened more than once—separate families of cold-blooded reptiles separately became separate families of warm-blooded mammals—there is no reason to rule out the chance that men, or creatures very like men, have evolved on other worlds.

The researches of the Leakeys in Africa have also shown us that there were several different manlike creatures existing at the same time several million years ago. It seems likely that if humans didn't evolve from one line of apes, they would have evolved from another, and if not from them, then from other mammals with hands, like opossums or racoons.

The chances are that the inhabitants of a SuperWorld, if they are not machines, will walk upright and have two hands and two eyes in front of their heads. They may be green, they may be hairless, their ears may resemble spinach leaves, but they will be "human."

# 10: SuperWorlds

Now let us think about the technological civilizations that have survived. In other words, about our future, if we are able to get through the next hundred years.

We can project the lines of our accomplishments up to now into the future. Our future, as far ahead as we can conceive, is the present of some SuperWorld.

One convenient way to measure a civilization is by the amount of energy it uses. Until two centuries ago, human civilization used animal power, including human muscle power, a small amount of air power (windmills, sailing ships), and water power (water wheels). We can be generous and say that before the nineteenth century, the total annual expenditure of energy amounted to about 50 million horsepower, or $4 \times 10^{17}$ ergs per second, or $11 \times 10^{24}$ ergs per year.

This system of notation, $10^{17}$, means a one followed by 17 zeroes. It is easier to comprehend than if it were written 100,000,-000,000,000,000. Using this system, 100 would be written $10^2$, 1,000 as $10^3$ and so on. It is also convenient, since multiplication can be performed simply by adding the exponents (the elevated numbers), and division by subtraction. For example: $10^2$ times $10^3 = 10^5$.

The erg is a unit of energy. It is a small unit, the amount of energy needed to move one gram (1/27 ounce), a distance of one centimeter (less than ½ inch).

A ton of hard coal contains 29 x $10^{16}$ ergs of energy. So if mankind, before the age of steam, was using 11 x $10^{24}$ ergs per year, the total energy at its disposal was the equivalent to that produced by about 40 million tons of hard coal. Today, our total energy use, measured in the same terms, is equivalent to energy produced by something less than 2 billion tons of hard coal a year. Thus, in less than two centuries, our energy use has increased almost 50 times.

Projecting a moderate rate of increase into the future, ⅔ of 1 percent a year, energy use will double in a century. At this rate, it will increase 1,000 times in a thousand years and 10 billion times in thirty-five hundred years (by the year A.D. 5500).

This raises a number of interesting questions. In the first place, we ought to pay some attention to the manner in which the yearly percentage growth takes place. This is difficult for us to grasp because we are used to thinking in linear—straight line—terms. We live in a daily world in which one and one make two, in which large numbers are reached only by much repetition. We think the only way to get from one to a thousand is by adding a thousand ones.

Biology doesn't work this way. When living things grow, they grow at *rates*, and the rates apply to the organism as it grows. This is how an almost microscopic egg becomes a human baby in nine months, increasing a billion times in size. To understand how this works we must understand the doubling of numbers. In its early stages, when its growth is fastest, each of the embryo's cells doubles every twenty-four hours. At the end of four days, the original single cell has become between twelve and thirty cells. Unlike linear growth, where the same number of units are added in each unit of time (building a brick house, for example), in doubling (exponential) growth, *more* units are added in each unit of time. One cell doubles into two. In the next time unit, there are two cells to double and we get four, having added two instead of one, as we would have in the linear system. In the next time unit there are four cells to double and we get eight, having added four instead of one, as in the linear system. Doubling can bring about an incredible increase in numbers in a short time, as the table below shows:

| Generation | # Exponential Units | # Linear Units |
|---|---|---|
| 1 | 1 | 1 |
| 2 | 2 | 2 |
| 3 | 4 | 3 |
| 4 | 8 | 4 |
| 5 | 16 | 5 |
| 6 | 32 | 6 |
| 7 | 64 | 7 |
| 8 | 128 | 8 |
| 9 | 256 | 9 |
| 10 | 512 | 10 |
| 11 | 1024 (about 1000) | 11 |
| 12 | 2000 | 12 |
| 13 | 4000 | 13 |
| 14 | 8000 | 14 |
| 15 | 16000 | 15 |
| 16 | 32000 | 16 |
| 17 | 64000 | 17 |
| 18 | 128000 | 18 |
| 19 | 256000 | 19 |
| 20 | 512000 | 20 |
| 21 | 1024000 | 21 |

Just twenty generations of doubling result in a millionfold growth.

All biological growth takes place in this manner. Not that all our cells keep doubling during the nine months we are in the womb. If that happened we would be shaped like volley balls. The cells take on different functions and double at different rates, but this is the system they use. Since our growth and that of all other living creatures is exponential, we may wonder how it is that the biological world around us appears quite stable. What stabilizes nature are limited resources: food, air, water, sunlight. A population of animals or plants can increase only while there is a supply of food or (in the case of most plants) the things it can make food out of.

Life also regulates itself by the way different life forms act on each other. Wolves, for example, keep the deer population from getting too big. Were there no wolves preying on the deer, the deer might destroy their food supply by removing rings of bark from all the trees in a forest. The relationship between wolves and deer

makes it possible for a fairly constant number of deer to survive year after year, instead of allowing an explosive increase in deer, followed by famine and perhaps death of all deer.

The web of life protects species at the expense of individuals; and life, itself, at the expense of species.

We may soon be turning asteroids (small planets) into colonies in space. A small cylinder, 300 feet long and 600 feet in diameter, could house 2,000 people. Bigger colonies could house millions. They could be self-sufficient, deriving all their energy from the sun, which never "sets" in space. Artificial gravity would be produced on the inner surface by rotation. In a cylinder shape, gravity would be uniform except at the top and bottom, where there would be none. Inside a sphere, it would be greatest at the equator and diminish to zero at the poles. Dr. Gerald K. O'Neill has suggested that the colonies be parked at the stable Lagrangian points, where Earth and Moon gravity are in balance, located at 60° on each side of the moon.

Earth algae would turn carbon dioxide into oxygen, cooling the surface of Venus and starting a process that could bring about Earthlike conditions. First, however, a way will have to be found to form a magnetic field to protect Venus from dangerous sun particles.

Millions of kinds of animals have become extinct in the past—many more kinds of animals than exist in the present. One reason why many of them may have disappeared could have been uncontrolled growth, a failure of balance. The growth of the billions of cells that compose our bodies is similarly regulated by natural controls. When these controls fail and a cell keeps doubling without stopping, we call the condition cancer.

The term cancer can be applied to large-scale events as well as small. Any uncontrolled doubling process can be called cancerous. In this sense, the present rate of human population growth is cancerous. Human population has already reached a point where there is barely enough food for adequate nutrition, and its doubling rate is less than thirty years.

Similarly, our energy-growth rate, if continued, will surpass the energy capacity of the planet. We are presently using energy mostly from fossil fuels (coal and oil) at a bit less than $2 \times 10^{19}$ ergs per second. The sun, by contrast, is broadcasting energy into space at a rate of $4 \times 10^{33}$ ergs per second, or at $10^{14}$ (10 followed by 14 zeroes, or 100 trillion) times the amount we now use. By the year 7000 however, the energy at our command could equal the total output of the sun. Even a total energy output of 1 percent of our one sun, an amount we should have at our disposal by the year 6200 would, if confined to Earth, destroy the planet. The heat would burn off the oceans and the atmosphere.

Clearly then, if we are to use energies of this magnitude in the future, we will not be using them on our native planet. Professor Freeman Dyson, of the Institute for Advanced Study in Princeton, New Jersey, has conceived that with such vast energy at our disposal, we could create an enlarged habitable space. The same idea also had occurred previously to the Russian rocket pioneer K. E. Tsiolkovskii.

Tsiolkovskii imagined that most of the solar system could be transformed to adapt more places in which humans could live comfortably. Mars could be moved closer to the sun, for example, and be given a richer atmosphere. Mercury and Venus could be moved farther from the sun. Asteroids—tens of thousands of small planets located mostly between the orbits of Mars and Jupiter—could be made into small inhabited worlds, and so on.

Dyson had an even more startling idea. The planet Jupiter has a diameter of about 10 times that of Earth. He calculated that the amount of matter in that giant planet was equal to that which would be contained in a spherical shell about 10 feet thick with a radius of 1 AU. With enough energy at our disposal, we could break up Jupiter and redistribute the pieces into millions of small worlds the same distance from the sun as Earth. With air and water and all the light of the sun (only 1/10 billionth part of which now falls on Earth) there would be living space for about $10^{23}$ people. (Present Earth population is less than $4 \times 10^{9}$.)

Others have proposed that advances in biological knowledge will enable us to adapt ourselves and other living things to new environments. For example, some think that some miles below the top of Jupiter's atmosphere there may be a region warmed by the giant planet and by sunlight trapped by high clouds having a comfortable temperature and liquid water. Plants could be developed to transform the ammonia-methane atmosphere to one consisting of free oxygen and nitrogen, in which case a large habitable zone could be created some miles above the planet's surface. Humans could either adapt to the planet's strong gravity (a 150-pound man would weigh almost 400 pounds) or be adapted to it by biological engineering. They might be given wings to fly in the dense atmosphere. It would be wrong, of course, to change Jupiter's atmosphere if we discovered that the planet already had evolved life forms of its own.

We cannot be sure that such great tasks will be feasible or that, in fact, we will be able to harness ever-increasing quantities of energy. Nature puts limits on exponential growth. Not only is our planet Earth limited in the number of beings it can support, there is even a limit to the amount of energy in the galaxy, a limit that would be approached, given the present doubling rate, by the year A.D. 11,000.

All space at the distance of Earth from the sun is colonized, using Jupiter as raw material.

HALE OBSERVATORIES PHOTOGRAPH

Another galactic twin, in the constellation of the Great Bear. Has it evolved Superbeings, capable of harnessing all its energy?

Also, when we start talking about using energy equal to the total output of stars, we may find this energy most useful in forms we cannot tolerate as humans. X-rays, gamma rays, ultraviolet and other forms of invisible EM radiation are dangerous to living tissue. If the surface of Earth were not shielded from these wavelengths by ozone, water vapor, and carbon dioxide in the atmosphere, life would not exist here.

Humans might, of course, manipulate these and other dangerous forms of energy from a safe distance. And there are other possibilities.

# 11: SuperBeings

There is nothing known at present that rules out the creation of artificial intelligence. Since their development in 1946 by J. Presper Eckert and John W. Mauchly, electronic computers have increased almost a million times in speed and at least that in storage capacity.

It seems that the capacity of the human brain derives from its ability to store information and its possession of multiple channels of communication between storage units. Intelligence grows out of the modes (programs; that is, language) it uses.

The cortex of the human brain, where reasoning takes place, contains about 10 billion cells, each with 1 to 10,000 connections, operating at speeds of up to about a city block a second. Present-day computers can store about 1,000 billion bits of information on magnetic disks in about ten wall cabinets. This information can be retrieved at very high speeds. It is predicted that within the next century, ways will be found to store the same amount of information in a cube smaller than a grain of rice.

Terry Winograd, a graduate student at MIT, has recently developed a computer program that closely duplicates the reasoning process of the human mind. The program uses only a million bits of information. By way of comparison, humans acquire information at the rate of about 100 bits per second, or about a million per day. So the computer, with only a million bits in its program, has only a limited amount of information. The world Winograd has invented for it is a world of a few children's toys and a few ideas: *solid body, one body supporting another, something can be in a box, right* and *left, up* and *down, backward* and *forward.*

Entering this little world—that is, using Winograd's program—a human can converse intelligently with the computer. "What does the box contain?" the person types in English.

"The blue pyramid and the blue box," the computer answers.

"How many blocks are not in the box?"

"Four of them," the machine says.

"Is at least one of them narrower than the one I told you to pick up?"

"Yes, the red cube."

Later, the person asks, "Is there a steeple?"

The computer answers, "Sorry, I don't know the word 'steeple.' "

The man explains, "A steeple is a stack which contains two green cubes and a pyramid, for example."

"I understand," the computer says.

"Are there any steeples now?"

"No."

"Build one."

The machine puts its mechanical hand out and moves the cubes around and builds the steeple.

At another point, the man asks the computer to explain what it is doing. "When did you pick up the pyramid?"

"While I was stacking up the red cube, the large red block, and the green cube."

"Why?"

"To get rid of it," the computer answers.

"Why did you do that?"

"To clear off the red cube."

"Why did you clear off that cube?"

"To put it on the large green cube."

When it runs out of reasons to explain its actions, the computer finally answers, "Because you asked me to."

There is no reason to doubt that computers with storage capacities in excess of the human brain, and with at least as many connecting paths, will be built. With suitable programs, these computers will exceed human intelligence.

It is also theoretically possible to design computers to build other computers. Indeed, a computer could be programmed to build a whole world of computers and machinery to mine, transport, and manufacture anything. A computer of this sort could be compared with a biological egg that is programmed to create an alligator, a palm tree, or a man, out of sugar, water, and a few other nutrients.

We may be remembered in self-reproducing machines, as fish are remembered in us.

The program of a biological egg is contained in the genetic material in the center (nucleus) of the cell. It is written in the form of giant molecules called cistrons. The letters are purines and pyramidines that form 3-letter words. There are about 4,000 letters in each cistron, making about 1,300 words. These 1,300 words are the instructions for creating or regulating one part of the entire animal or plant. The individual cistrons reside in the cells as part of long

For "life support" artificial intelligences need only the raw energy of the universe. They may already have mastered entire galaxies.

chains of cistrons called chromosomes. The human cell contains about a million cistrons arranged in 46 chromosomes. One fertilized egg, barely visible, contains the entire program for making a human being in more than a billion 3-letter words. It is a machine for transplanting these words into nerves, blood, bone, skin, and the enzymes that regulate and control.

The new thirty-volume Encyclopaedia Britannica contains 43

million words. With their billion or so words, the 46 microscopic human chromosomes contain as much information as at least two dozen sets of the Britannica.

A living cell has a nucleus and a non-nuclear cytoplasm. The nucleus contains patterns for regulating the cell and for making other cells. The cytoplasm has the machinery of the cell, the devices for detecting food, for moving, and for converting food into usable energy. The nucleus of the computer, its pattern, is the program, originated on magnetic tape by a human. The computer's cytoplasm is its apparatus of transistors, switches, and other electronic devices, typewriters, and tapes with which the program is transformed into usable information, either printed out or applied by some process, including, possibly, the making of another computer.

With intelligence, awareness, sense organs (television cameras as eyes, microphones as ears), the computer may represent the end of evolution. We may be creating our successors, as every form of life in the long road from the primeval soup has created its successors. Computers are better adapted than human beings to a future world of stellar energies and exploration among the stars. They can exist in a vacuum, they would be able to withstand hard radiation, and their lifetimes would be unlimited.

Once computers achieve purposeful self-awareness and the ability to reproduce themselves, they will no longer need humans. We may be left behind, on Earth and a few other planets, while they depart for the stars.

The future may belong to them.

# 12: Looking for SuperWorlds

Let us assume that there are 1 million SuperWorlds in our galaxy. How can we find them?

The disk, in which we will start our search, contains about 20 billion stars. A million is 1/20,000th of 20 billion. We will have to examine 20,000 stars in order to find our SuperWorld.

In our part of the galaxy the density of stars is about one per 12 cubic parsecs. The volume of space holding 20,000 stars would be a sphere with a radius of 62 parsecs.

The nearest SuperWorld is no more than 62 parsecs distant.

To find it, we will not have to examine every one of the 20,000 nearest stars. We could begin by eliminating stars that we believe to be unlikely sites of life. In Chapter 8 we saw that after eliminating double stars and those that were too big, too small, or too old, we were left with only one good possibility, Tau Ceti, among the fifty-five stars nearest us. Applying similar standards, we could narrow the search to perhaps 1,000 good prospects.

How will we detect the SuperWorld? A number of astronomers and physicists have suggested that we listen for intelligent radio signals. Radio waves between 1 centimeter and 300 meters in length can penetrate Earth's atmosphere. The shorter end of this range, between 3 and 30 centimeters, is particularly well suited for interstellar communication. There is the least amount of natural interference in galactic space at these wavelengths.

Short wave radio signals broadcast by Guglielmo Marconi, Nikola Tesla, and other radio pioneers at the turn of the century have already traveled more than 70 light years (21.5 parsecs) into space and may have reached a SuperWorld. Whether or not such signals are detected by them will depend on their receiving apparatus. If they have left a probe in or near the solar system, the probe would almost certainly have picked up the signals and relayed them to its home base. If there were no probe, only an incredibly sensitive receiver would be able to detect them on a distant planet. EM radiation diminishes in strength by the square of the distance traveled. A signal that has traveled 21.5 parsecs will be only $10^{-29}$ (a decimal in which the numeral one is preceded by 28 zeroes) as powerful as it was 1 mile from the broadcasting point.

We do not have equipment on Earth capable of detecting a signal that weak. We have been sending much stronger signals during the past thirty years. The 1,000 foot Arecibo radar in Puerto Rico, for example, sent out a signal strong enough to be detected by existing Earth radio telescopes at a distance of 2,000 parsecs, that is, if the telescope was aimed in exactly the right direction. And the newest equipment at Arecibo has extended the range to 20,000 parsecs (20 kiloparsecs). Since the galaxy is only about 30 kiloparsecs across, this equipment puts us in range of any other planet in the galaxy with a radio telescope of equal or greater size.

A SuperWorld that wanted to make its presence known would broadcast powerful signals in all directions. To do this it would need to use an amount of energy equal to one thousandth the output of a star like our sun. We have already estimated that our civilization should have power resources equal to the output of our sun by the year A.D. 7000. At that time, by diverting just a thousandth of our energy resources to interstellar communication, we should

THE NATIONAL ASTRONOMY AND IONOSPHERE CENTER'S ARECIBO OBSERVATORY, OPERATED BY CORNELL UNIVERSITY UNDER CONTRACT WITH THE NATIONAL SCIENCE FOUNDATION

The thousand-foot radio-telescope at Arecibo, Puerto Rico. Its signals will be detectable by similar instruments out to a distance of 20 kiloparsecs, that is, through most of our galaxy.

be able to send out powerful signals that would cross a distance of 13 kiloparsecs in every direction.

A search of the galaxy with our most powerful radio telescopes should, therefore, after a few years, tell us whether there are any SuperWorlds advertising their presence in the galaxy.

The same amount of power could also be used to beam a message that could be detected more than a megaparsec away. The beam could be wide enough to cover the entire galaxy in Andromeda, which is only about half this distance away. Similarly, a radio telescope aimed at that galaxy would tell us if any SuperWorld there is aiming a strong signal at our galaxy. Two-way communication by radio between galaxies would, however, hardly be practical. The 600-kiloparsec distance between our galaxy and the one in Andromeda represents about 2 million light years. It would take 4 million years to send a message to Andromeda and receive a reply.

SuperWorlds could, of course, be detected by eavesdropping as well as by receiving especially beamed messages. Eavesdropping would mean listening in on radio communications—messages to space ships or from one planet to another. Since these would neither be beamed at Earth nor powerfully broadcast with the intention of being received at great distances, much more sensitive receiving equipment would be needed to find them. Indeed, since such transmissions would be sent by narrow beams to save energy, it might be impossible to eavesdrop unless beams were going out in many hundreds of different directions to other SuperWorlds.

If, on the other hand, we were just to look for messages especially directed at us, we would have to figure out the frequency at which the SuperWorld would be broadcasting. There are 9 billion different frequencies between 3 centimeter and 30 centimeter wavelengths, the best wavelengths to use for interstellar communication.

In 1959, Dr. Philip Morrison of MIT and Dr. Guiseppe Cocconi of Cornell proposed, in the British science journal *Nature*, that SuperWorlds might be beaming messages into space at 1420 million cycles per second; that is, at a wavelength of 21 centimeters. They proposed this wavelength because it is the wavelength of neutral hydrogen. It would be logical to assume that powerful radio telescopes would be tuned into this wavelength, so useful for astronomical purposes. Others have proposed that searches be made at wavelengths within the 3 to 30 centimeter range that are multiples of 21 centimeters: 10.5 centimeters, 5.25 centimeters, and 26.25 centimeters; and at the wavelengths of other substances commonly found in space, and their multiples.

In 1960, the year after the Morrison-Cocconi suggestion, Dr. Frank Drake of Cornell aimed the 85-foot radio telescope at Green Bank, West Virginia, at what he considered to be the two most promising nearby stars, Tau Ceti and Epsilon Eridani. He detected no signals at the 21 centimeter wavelength. In the fall of 1968, four Soviet radio astronomers searched Tau Ceti, Epsilon Eridani, a small M-type dwarf in the Big Dipper, and eight other G type stars out to a distance of 19 parsecs. They checked twenty-five different wavelengths, from the 21 centimeter hydrogen line to 30 centimeters, for each star. They also tuned in on the galaxy in Andromeda, 600 kiloparsecs away. At that distance the entire galaxy appears so small that it was possible for them to listen to billions of stars at a time. (A broadcast signal would also, of course, have to be immensely stronger to be detected over that distance.) They heard nothing from the eleven stars in this galaxy or from Andromeda.

In October, 1971, another astronomer, G. L. Verschuur, listened to ten close stars on the hydrogen wavelength, using the National Radio Astronomy Observatory's 140 and 300 foot antennas at Green Bank; and in the past few years this search has been widened to include some five hundred nearby stars, all the most likely suns within about 25 parsecs. So far, no signals have been heard. Plans are now being developed to scan thousands of stars over hundreds of wavelengths, with the help of a computer when the new galactic-range radio telescope, the Very Large Array, is available in New Mexico in 1981.

What will an intelligent signal be? It will be a code. Our attention would be attracted, for example, to any regular sequence of signals, and a repetition of the sequence. A lot of information, including crude television pictures, could be transmitted just by sequences of numbers. As an example of how this would work, Dr.

1111000010100100001100100000000100000010100
1000001100101100111100000011000011010000000
001000000100000100000100010101000001000000000
00000000000100010000000000001011000000000000
00000001000111011010110101000000000000000000
00001001000011101010101000000000101010101
000000000111010101011101011000000001000000
00000000000010000000000000010001001111111000
0011101000000101100000011100000000100000000000
10000000001000000001111100000001011000101110
100000000110010111110101111100010011111001
0000000000001111100000001011000111111100000
100000011000000110000100000110000000011000101
0010001111100101111

The American radio-astronomer, Dr. Frank Drake of Cornell University, devised this as a possible SuperWorld message, transmitted in digital form (1's or 0's). The problem—as it was for Galle and Talon in May 1929—is to decipher it.

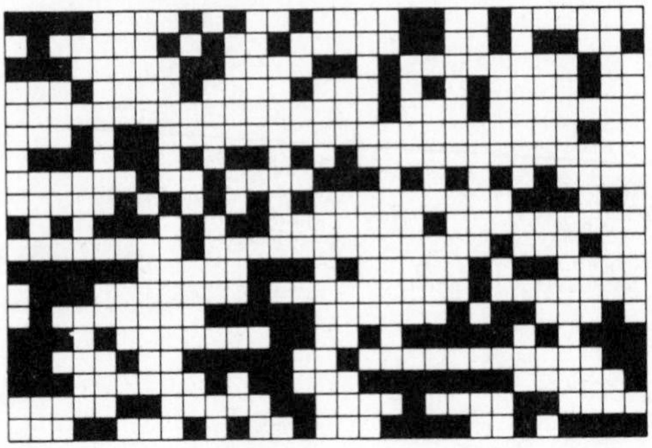

The message is repeated. Each sequence consists of 551 symbols (bits). The 1's are filled in, the 0's left blank, and they are arranged in 19 rows each with 29 characters. No sense can be made out of this solution.

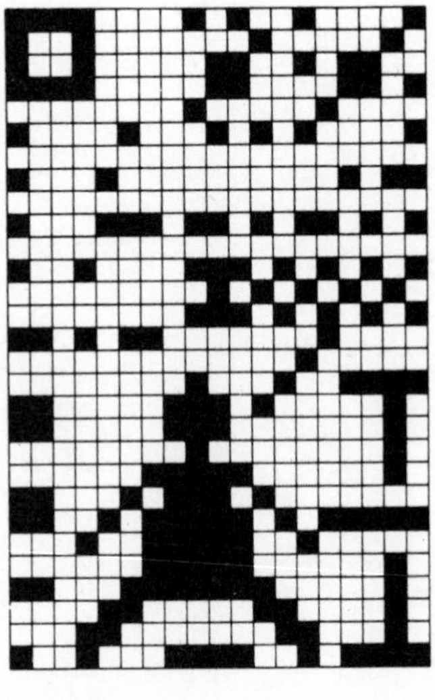

Now the bits are arranged in 29 rows of 19 characters. The "television" picture shows us the SuperWorld creature, its solar system, and chemistry. It even gives its "name"; (the symbols 1,1,1,1, represented by four black squares between its legs).

REPRODUCED BY PERMISSION FROM "INTELLIGENT LIFE IN THE UNIVERSE," BY I.S. SHKLOVSKII AND CARL SAGAN (HOLDEN DAY, SAN FRANCISCO, 1966; DELL PUBLISHING COMPANY, NEW YORK, 1967).

Drake has proposed that a SuperWorld might broadcast prime numbers (unusual numbers that cannot be divided by any number other than one: 1,3,5,7,11,13,17,19. . . .).

Drake suggested that the SuperWorld might send out a signal made out of the product of two prime numbers, for example 551, the product of 29 and 19. This would tell us that a picture is to be made out of 29 lines, each with 19 bits of information.

Other ways of communicating over long distances would be by

lasers—narrow beams of high-energy light—or by probes, small automated space ships. Lasers, confining energy to a narrow beam, can be seen over great distances. A laser with no more power than an ordinary flashlight has been seen on the moon from Earth. Lasers using other parts of the EM spectrum, like x-rays or gamma rays, could be seen through the galactic center. Many objects in the heavens broadcast radio waves, which makes it harder to find intelligent signals. This would not be a problem with laser beams, which can only be produced artificially.

The reason the Australian astronomer Ronald Bracewell suggested that we ought to look for probes was that this would be a cheaper way of communicating with other worlds than by direct radio contact. A SuperWorld wanting to contact another civilization within 30 parsecs, he wrote, might have to send signals to one thousand stars. If it beamed the signals to save power, it would have to set up one thousand antennas to broadcast at more than a million watts of power for one hundred thousand or a million years. It would be more practical to send out one thousand probes, each programmed to orbit a star at the distance at which life-bearing planets would be expected. From within the planet's solar system, low-powered receiving and sending equipment would be sufficient to establish communication.

Such a probe might orbit the star for centuries, listening over the EM spectrum for signs of intelligence. With a computer on board, the probe could talk to the detected civilization and relay information back to the SuperWorld.

It is surprising how little evidence of life can be seen from space, even from quite near a planet. Studies of Earth by astronauts, and thousands of daylight photographs taken from just a few hundred miles altitude, show no evidence of life or the presence of man. The glow of cities can be seen at night, and analysis of the light could reveal its artificial nature, so this would be one way of detecting civilization from near space. But more than a century ago even this evidence would have been lacking.

Except for listening for radio signals, we so far have developed no way of detecting life on other planets from space, but it is likely that we shall do so before the end of the century. One possible way of doing this, which might be employed by a SuperWorld probe, would be to scan the atmosphere. A considerable oxygen content would be evidence of the existence of plant life, and methane from the bowels of grazing animals (there were 60 million bison on the American plains two hundred years ago) would indicate the presence of land animals.

When Duncan Lunan reported his interpretation of the Hals, Störmer, Van der Pol sequences, Ronald Bracewell analyzed them. Treating the first picture Lunan got of the constellation Boötes as made from 13 lines, each with 9 bits of information, this meant there were 117 squares (9 x 13) in which stars could be placed. If a constellation consisted of five stars and all five were placed in exactly the right squares, this would be convincing evidence of an intelligent message because, with all the possible places in which five stars could be put among the 117 squares, the chances were only 1 in 100,000 that they would indeed make a constellation. Six stars in the right places would be even more convincing, and so on.

Because Epsilon Boötes was missing and Arcturus was out of position, the constellation Boötes did not meet this test. This was not to say that Lunan's ideas were wrong, but the map could not stand as evidence by itself.

Lunan kept seeking more information. A good place for a probe to park itself near the Earth would be at the distance of the moon and 60 degrees either in front or behind it. The orbit of the moon can be thought of as a circle going around the Earth. A circle has 360 degrees, 60 degrees represents a sixth of the way around this circle. The two points on the circle located 60 degrees from the moon are places where the gravity of the Earth and the moon cancel each other out. A probe placed in either of these positions could remain there for thousands of years with a minimum of effort.

Checking the times at which echoes were heard, Lunan found that they were almost always when at least one of these Lagrangian points, as they are called, was in the sky. The records favored the Trailing Point, the one that follows the moon in its orbit around Earth, indicating that something there was connected to the echoes.

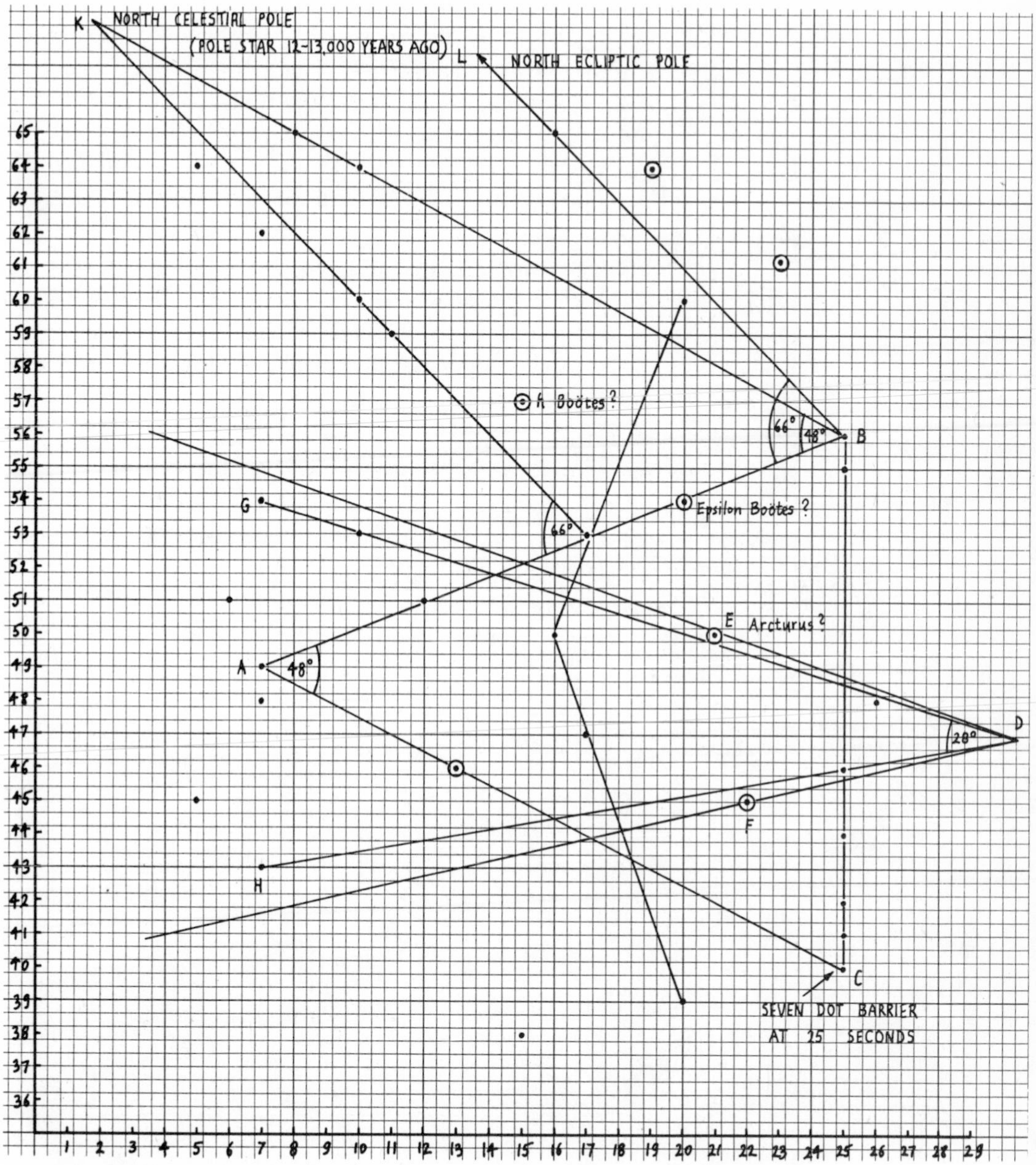


Lunan chart made from additional echo records of October 24, 1928, shows another Boötes figure with Arcturus (A) as it was 13,000 years ago. Angle GDH is 28°, the height of Boötes in the sky as seen from Earth.

Lunan also kept trying to locate more complete records of the echo sequences that Hals and Störmer had heard. On the basis of a partial record of echoes received by Hals on the 24th of October, 1928, Lunan had constructed a second star map showing several constellations near Boötes. He hoped that if he found the rest of that night's sequence, he would be able to use it either to support or to disprove his ideas. In December, 1973, more details on the October 24th echoes were found. These showed that Lunan's second map was wrong.

A new map, prepared from the more complete and accurate information, proved to be similar to the first map, but with more information. Like the first map, the new second map had a vertical row of dots to the left and a constellation to the right. The first map showed Boötes with Epsilon Boötes missing and Arcturus displaced. In this second map Arcturus was located in the same position it had occupied in the first map, but Epsilon was in the right

Chart from Hals data of February 18, 1929. Reference lines and Boötes-like figures could be caused by an unknown natural process or, in some cases, by Lunan, who decided which dots signified stars and which were reference points.

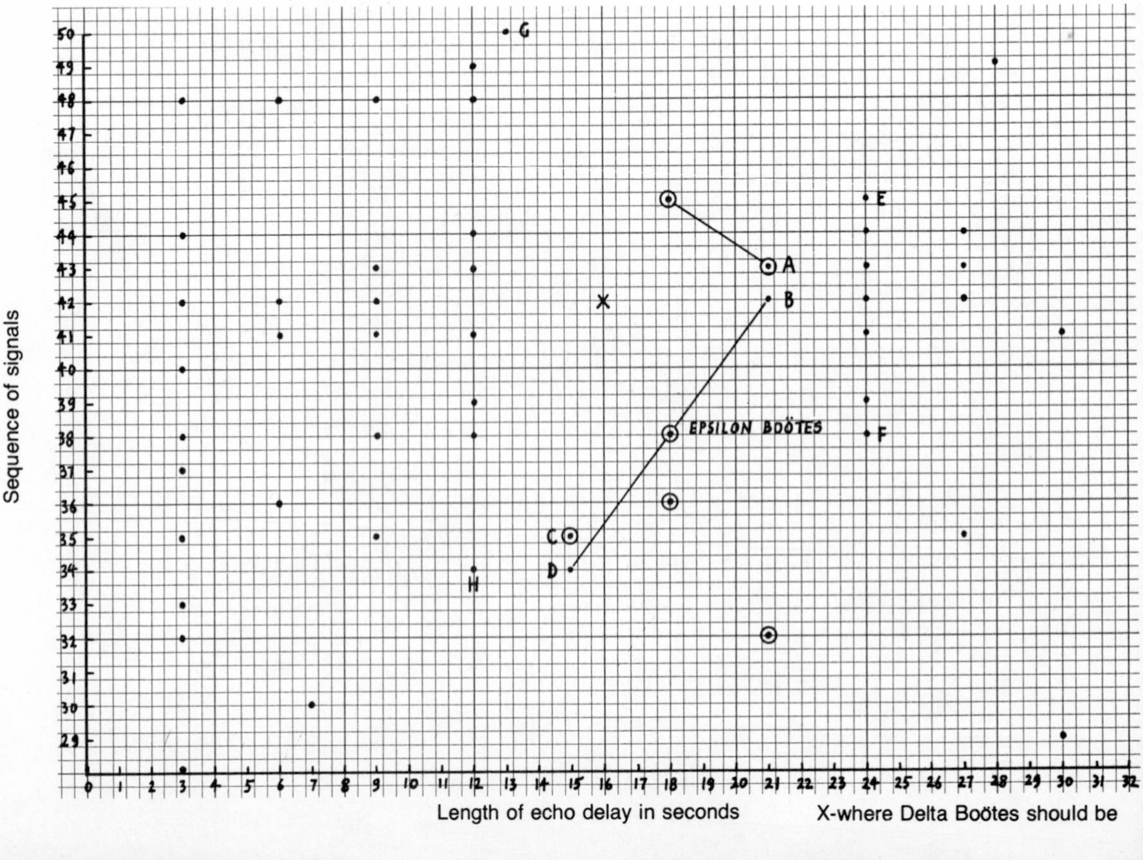

place. Extra lines passing through Epsilon gave its position with regard to two points in the sky. These showed that the stars in the constellation were where they had been 13,000 years ago.

It was often not possible to obtain echoes. Störmer supposed this was because interference from the sun usually affected Earth's atmosphere in such a way that 31.4 meter waves could not get through to outer space. The next occasion on which the sun was quiet enough to permit further experiments was in the middle of February, 1929. On the 18th, a long series of echoes was received. In this case, several echoes at intervals that were multiples of 3 seconds followed each signal, so that more information was received than before. One signal, for example, brought echoes at 3 seconds and at 21 seconds. Another, at 3, 9, 12, 18, and 24 seconds. Again, the echoes could be used to construct a map with a vertical line on the left and a Boötes-like constellation on the right. Only this time, Delta Boötes was missing, and the Arcturus dot was closer to its present position.

Reference lines on the map led Lunan to conclude that the constellation's stars were in the position it had occupied 6,500 years ago. The position of Arcturus was also the position it had had at that time. In other words, the time of the third map was halfway between the present day and the time of the first two maps.

Lunan thinks that in October, 1928, when the Dutch station at Eindhoven began broadcasting signals at twenty-second intervals instead of five-second intervals, the probe understood this to mean that its presence, made known by its echo answers to the five-second signals, was recognized. The probe understood the increased spacing of signals as a request for information, to be given in varied delay-time echoes. On October 10, 1928, it sent the first Boötes map.

When the spacing between signals was increased to thirty seconds on the night of October 24th, the probe again understood this as a request for more information and transmitted the second, more detailed, map.

The next signals, on February 18, 1929, sent at the same regular intervals, indicated to the probe that its first two maps were not understood. It therefore transmitted a third map, updated 6,500 years.

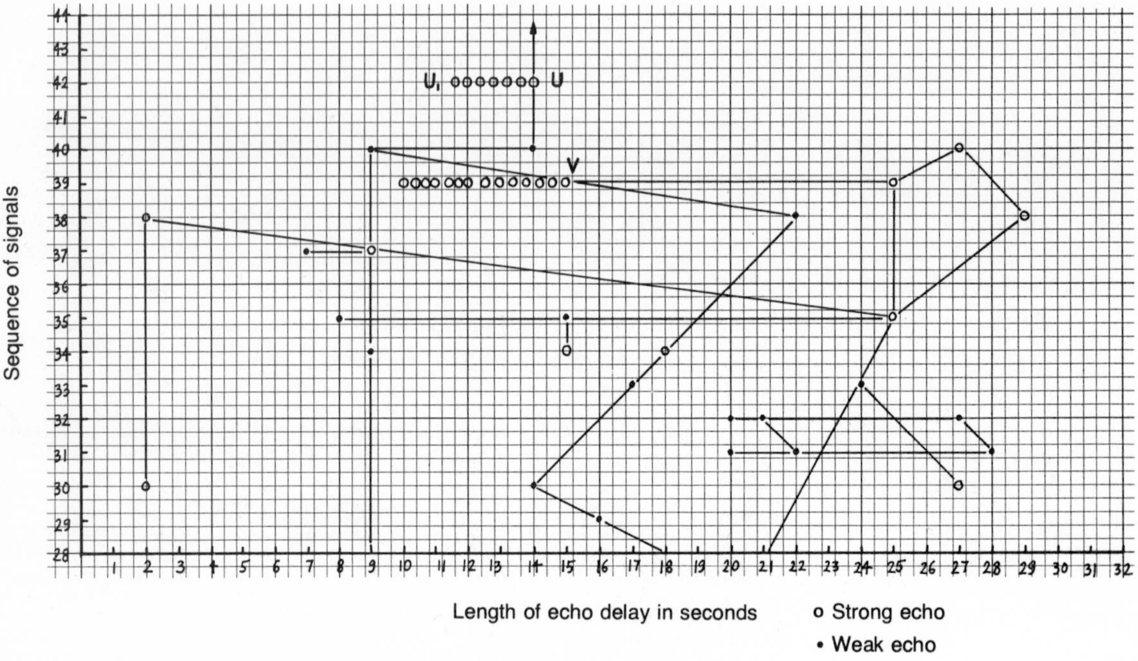


A portion of the same echo sequence, recorded by Galle and Talon in May, 1929, that appears on page 14. The original Galle–Talon chart appears below. Above, it has been turned around by Lunan so that the echo-delay scale is horizontal and the time is vertical. A Boötes figure now appears at the right.

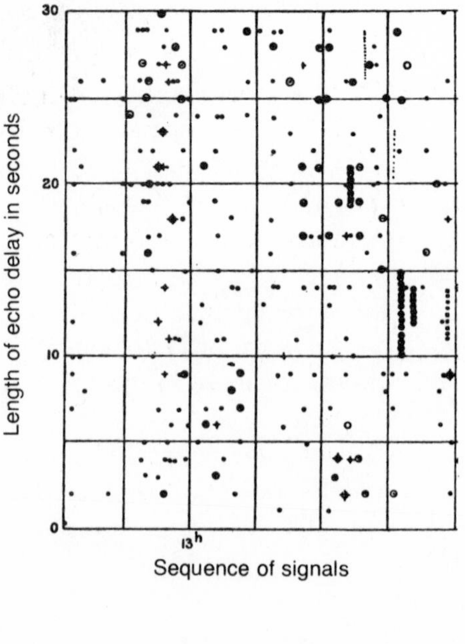

Ten days later, when Eindhoven started sending coded signals, the probe stopped sending maps. But in May, when the French signals, at a different wavelength and using musical tones, were picked up by the probe, it sent a fourth map, which showed Arcturus in both its former and present positions.

The absence of Delta Boötes from the third map has caused Lunan to recast his thinking about the probe's origin. He decided, instead of looking at them as maps showing where the probe came from, to look at them as maps used by the probe in navigating here. In that case, Epsilon Boötes and Delta Boötes might have been left out because they might have appeared much less bright at the place the probe set out from.

It turned out that from the positions of two nearby stars, Epsilon Eridani and Tau Ceti, Epsilon Boötes would appear a lot dimmer than it does from Earth. Also, Delta Boötes, quite similar to Epsilon, was much less bright a few thousand years ago.

The next question was: Where would our sun appear, viewed from Epsilon Eridani and Tau Ceti? From Epsilon Eridani it would appear near the constellation Leo Minor. From Tau Ceti, our sun would appear to be in Boötes, quite near the star Tau Boötes. Furthermore, as a ship approached our sun from Tau Ceti, Arcturus, Epsilon Boötes, and Delta Boötes would form a straight line. A probe could use three stars as a guide to our sun.

Tau Ceti is a G 4 type star, a bit smaller than our sun but otherwise much like it. As stated in Chapter 8, it is the most likely of the nearer stars to possess an Earthlike planet.

Lunan also found it interesting that Marconi, in 1921, had reported receiving signals from outer space that he had broadcast in 1899. The interval from 1899 to 1921 is 22 years. Assuming the probe picked up those signals and rebroadcast them to its home base, which then sent a return signal instructing the probe to repeat the message, how long would this take? Tau Ceti is estimated to be about 11.9 light years from Earth (3.2 parsecs). The signal would take 11.9 years to reach Tau Ceti, and 11.9 years to return. That would be 23.8 years for the round trip. This is somewhat longer than the interval reported by Marconi, but our estimate of the distance of Tau Ceti may be inaccurate, or the home base may even be on a comet half a light year or more from the star.

If Lunan's ingenious ideas are correct, then something interesting will be found at one of the Lagrangian points on one side of the moon. The Apollo 14 astronauts tried to take a photograph of one of these points, but their film was fogged by radiation coming from there.

Meanwhile, two Soviet researchers, Nikolai Kardashev and Vsevelod Troitsky, are examining radio pulses they have picked up on a series of antennas 1,800 miles apart. The signals come in at different wavelengths, from 1 centimeter to a few hundred meters. Kardashev and Troitsky believe that the signals originate outside the Earth, from somewhere in the solar system. Their regular form and strict periodicity, Kardashev says, "make it possible to assume they were of artificial origin."

# 13: Traveling to SuperWorlds

Assuming that a probe came here from a SuperWorld some parsecs distant, how did it get here? As we have seen, a parsec is a tremendous distance by earthly standards, equal to 200,000 AUs. At present, travel just to the nearer parts of the solar system strains our resources. Landing a 15-ton lunar module on the moon, carrying two men, required a vehicle with a total weight at launch of 3,130 tons; 95 percent of which was fuel. The maximum speed attained was a little less than 7 miles a second. The velocity during most of the trip was less than this, so that it took two and one half days to reach the moon, a distance of 1/400th AU from Earth. Similar velocities permitted the 1 ton Mariner probe to reach Mars in five and one half months, after a voyage of about 2/3 AU.

One 570 pound probe of our own is on its way out of the solar system. Launched March 2, 1972, Pioneer 10 reached Jupiter twenty-one months later. After scanning the giant planet, it used Jupiter's gravity, according to plan, to twist it into a path that will take it out of the reach of the sun. Traveling at 7 miles a second, it will reach the orbit of Pluto, about 40 AUs from Earth, sometime in 1989. At this rate it will take 85,000 years to cover a parsec.

Surprisingly, it is already within our capacity to achieve considerably higher speeds, which would enable us to send a few men to the nearest star after a voyage of only 126 years. To do this, however, we would have to devote enormous resources to the project, which, it is estimated, would cost at least $100 billion.

This was worked out by Freeman Dyson and Theodore B. Taylor in connection with a government project on the use of nuclear energy in space travel. A 50,000 ton ship would be accelerated to 1/18th the speed of light by the explosion of 150,000 hydrogen bombs, one every three seconds for about five days. At this speed, the ship would travel 1.3 parsecs to Alpha Centauri in about 126 years. It would take 325 years to reach Tau Ceti, which, not being part of a multiple star system, would seem to be a more sensible objective. The time to Tau Ceti could be cut to eighty years if the ship weighed only 10,000 tons and about 60 times as many bombs were used; but this of course would be a great deal more expensive.

Having reached the vicinity of the destination star, the big ship would slow down by the explosion of another 150,000 bombs. Since there would be no bombs left for a return journey, this would be a one-way mission.

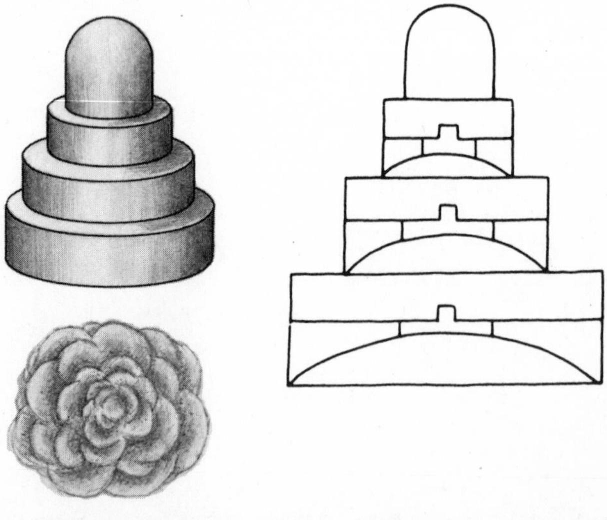

A 160 foot ship, powered by 2,000 atom bombs, could take a crew of 150 to Mars in three months. Multi-stage ships would be needed for interstellar voyages. Work stopped on these vessels when a 1963 treaty banned atomic explosions in space.

The ship would contain everything needed to colonize a planet, along with radio equipment to beam back to Earth messages about what was found. Unless some method had been found to prolong or suspend life, the colonizers would be descendants of the original crew. Ten generations would have passed en route to Tau Ceti. Those that first set foot on the new planet would be as remote in time from those who departed Earth as we are from the Pilgrim fathers.

Of course the time required for trips to the stars would diminish if we were able to travel faster. The hydrogen-bomb-powered vessel achieves a maximum speed of 1/18th the speed of light. The fastest man has traveled yet is about 1/26,000th light speed, during the first few minutes of moon journeys. A ship accelerated to light speed would have travel times in light-year distances. Alpha Centauri, 4.3 light years away (1.3 parsecs), would be reached in 4.3 years. It would take only a bit more than ten years to reach Tau Ceti.

Offhand, it would seem that even this great speed would limit us to the vicinity of the sun if we are thinking in terms of trips that could be made within a man's lifetime. If a team of well-trained astronauts could last fifty years in space, light-speed travel would confine us to within 25 light years of the sun for round-trip journeys.

But we have been thinking in Earth-bound terms, ignoring the fact that the universe is far stranger than our senses can perceive. As pointed out in Chapter 3, light speed is the speed limit of the universe. We have also mentioned that mass and energy are different forms of the same thing, and that even space and time are not distinct.

The faster a body travels the more energy it has. The more energy it has, the greater its mass. As our ship accelerates its mass keeps increasing, thus requiring ever-greater amounts of power to achieve the same acceleration. The effect is small until the ship gets close to the speed of light.

All relativity effects are noticeable only at very high speeds, close to that of light. At these speeds, the translation of space into time becomes noticeable. The time system of the moving body slows. A second, on moving-body P, lasts longer than a second on body Q, if Q is moving more slowly than P.

The faster the ship travels, the longer the seconds on board, compared with seconds on Earth. At light speed, 186,000 miles per second, time on board ship would not move at all. This is unobtainable because at light speed the mass of the ship would be infinite and require an infinite force to accelerate it.

At speeds close to that of light, time would stretch out—dilate—very noticeably compared with Earth time. At 90 percent light speed, a second on Earth, $t_e$, will last only 44 percent as long as a second on the ship, $t_s$. At 99 percent light speed, $t_e$ will be only 14 percent $t_s$. Time on the ship will be passing seven times as slowly as time on Earth. Seven years will pass on Earth while one year passes on the ship. At 99.99 percent light speed, $t_e$ will be only 1.4 percent $t_s$, and so on.

The only humans so far to have recorded experiencing time dilation were two American physicists, Joseph Hafele and Richard Keating, who took a very accurate atomic clock with them on a round-the-world trip on a Jumbo jet. On their return to Washington, they found that the traveling clock was one one-hundred billionth of a second behind the atomic clocks they had left behind, as predicted by time-dilation theory. The amount of time slowing was tiny because their speed was so slow, compared with light.

Another surprising thing is that these high velocities can be reached quickly at accelerations that are comfortable for humans. The acceleration of Earth's gravity, to which we are all accustomed (1 g), is 32 feet per second per second. Acceleration means speeding up. Per second per second means that the speed, measured in feet per second, increases each second. A body accelerated 1 g will be moving at a velocity of 32 feet per second at the end of one second. At the end of two seconds it will be moving at a velocity of 64 feet per second (32 plus 32). At the end of three seconds it will be moving at a velocity of 96 feet per second (32 plus 32 plus 32), and so on. A ship accelerated constantly at 1 g would attain a speed of 1,000 miles per second in two days. It would approach light speed after one year of acceleration.

With half the trip used in acceleration and half for deceleration, and with time dilation at work, no part of the entire universe would be beyond the range of a single human lifetime. It would take twenty-one years, ship time, to reach the center of the galaxy, twenty-eight years to reach the galaxy in Andromeda, thirty-three years to reach the Virgo group of galaxies, and sixty to reach out three-quarters of a megaparsec, a quarter of the distance to the farthest object known.

From inside the star ship, the universe will appear curious. No matter how far the ship travels, the sun it left will never appear to be more than about 1 light year distant. Once it has covered half the distance to its destination, the destination will never appear to come closer than about 1 light year. To a ship traveling from here to the galaxy in Andromeda, our sun and that galaxy, after a year of travel, will seem to be only 2 light years apart, although they appear to us on Earth to be 2 million light years apart. As the crew approaches the destination, time as observed ahead will be speeded up. The crew en route to the Andromeda galaxy will observe 2 million years of Andromeda time during the final fourteen years of its voyage. Stars that, if observed from Earth, would be orbiting each other once a year would appear from the ship to be orbiting each other 143,000 times a year.

At maximum speed, however, they will have great difficulty in observing any such phenomena. As they reach 99 percent light speed their velocity will cause Doppler shifts in the light from the stars. (Waves coming toward a moving receiver seem to be shorter by an amount proportional to the speed of the receiver.) This will be more noticeable when these stars are located in the line of flight, either directly ahead or behind the ship. The shift will move the wavelengths of light coming from stars directly ahead and behind, away from the visible spectrum, so nothing but a circle of blackness will be seen directly ahead. Around this circle will be a halo of the remaining stars, their colors in a rainbow from ultraviolet, nearest the dark circle in front of the ship, to infrared at the rainbow's outer limits. For navigational purposes, the stars ahead of the ship, now invisible, will have to be scanned by gamma-ray detectors.

In a sense all these voyages covering galactic distances will be one-way trips. The crew could return to Earth, but the Earth they returned to would be entirely different from the Earth they left. During these voyages time on Earth would continue at its usual pace, very swiftly compared with time on the ship. Returning from 50 light years out, the crew would find the Earth at least one hundred years older than when it left. A crew back from a one-thousand-light-year journey would find that two thousand years had passed on Earth during the ten-year ship time of the voyage. Were the crew to circumnavigate the universe, the Earth would no longer exist when the mission was completed, and the sun itself would be a feeble white dwarf, an unrecognizable cinder.

It is curious to find that the universe operates in such a way that every part of it is potentially open to human exploration and that the only requirement for this is an ability to accelerate at Earth gravity for part of a human lifetime.

Can such acceleration be achieved?

At present we can obtain accelerations of several gs for a couple of minutes. To provide this much boost to a 50-ton ship like an Apollo spacecraft, requires about 3,000 tons of fuel, burned at the rate of 15 tons a second. Even if there were some way of fueling a ship in space, where it could accelerate without fighting the full force of Earth's gravity, a 50-ton ship would need around 8-million tons of fuel to accelerate at 1 g for just one hour. This is using our present-day rocket fuels, chemical fuels, kerosene, liquid oxygen, and liquid hydrogen.

Suppose we were able to use the hydrogen-fusion reaction to fuel our ship? To accelerate a 10-ton ship at 1 g for a round trip at which 99 percent light speed is reached (a round trip demands four accelerations, an acceleration and a deceleration each way), would require 64-billion tons of hydrogen. The reaction in which matter and antimatter destroy themselves is 300 times more powerful than hydrogen fusion. It is the most powerful energy source imaginable. The same trip powered by matter and antimatter would require 400,000 tons of fuel. This does not seem to be an altogether unreasonable amount of fuel; but we do not know whether antimatter does exist in our universe or within a reasonable distance from Earth; and its manufacture and handling would be very difficult.

One solution to the problem presented by these enormous or dangerous fuel requirements is to design a ship that does not have to carry the fuel needed for its journey. A laser could be used to beam energy to a ship from the Earth or the moon. If the ship could be kept locked on the beam over parsec distances, the system could be used until the ship got close to light speed. At that point the ship would, in effect, be running away from the power supply, and the system would become decreasingly effective. A ship accelerated in this way would still have to carry the fuel required for deceleration.

Another possibility would be to find fuel along the way. The galaxy is full of hydrogen gas. The average density of hydrogen in the galaxy is 1 atom per cubic centimeter. In the disk, among the spiral arms, there are 10 atoms per cubic centimeter, and there are clouds with much higher concentrations. These are vacuums by Earth standards—the best vacuums produced on earth have about $10^{13}$ atoms per cubic centimeter; but in the vast dimensions of galactic space, even in these near-vacuum conditions, large amounts of hydrogen are involved.

The American engineer Robert W. Bussard has proposed that a ship traveling at high speed could scoop hydrogen out of space and use it as fuel. The amount of hydrogen scooped up per second would depend on the speed of the ship, the size of the collecting area, and the density of hydrogen in the region of space in which it traveled.

If the ship had a hydrogen-fusion engine capable of converting 0.1 percent of the hydrogen into energy, the scoop would have to be 20 million kilometers (12 million miles) in diameter when it was traveling at 18 miles a second. At 18,000 miles a second, the scoop could be 12,000 miles across. At 90 percent of light speed, 168,000 miles per second, the scoop could be 1,200 miles across. Obviously, the ship would have to be boosted to a considerable speed in order to avoid having to make the scoop impossibly large.

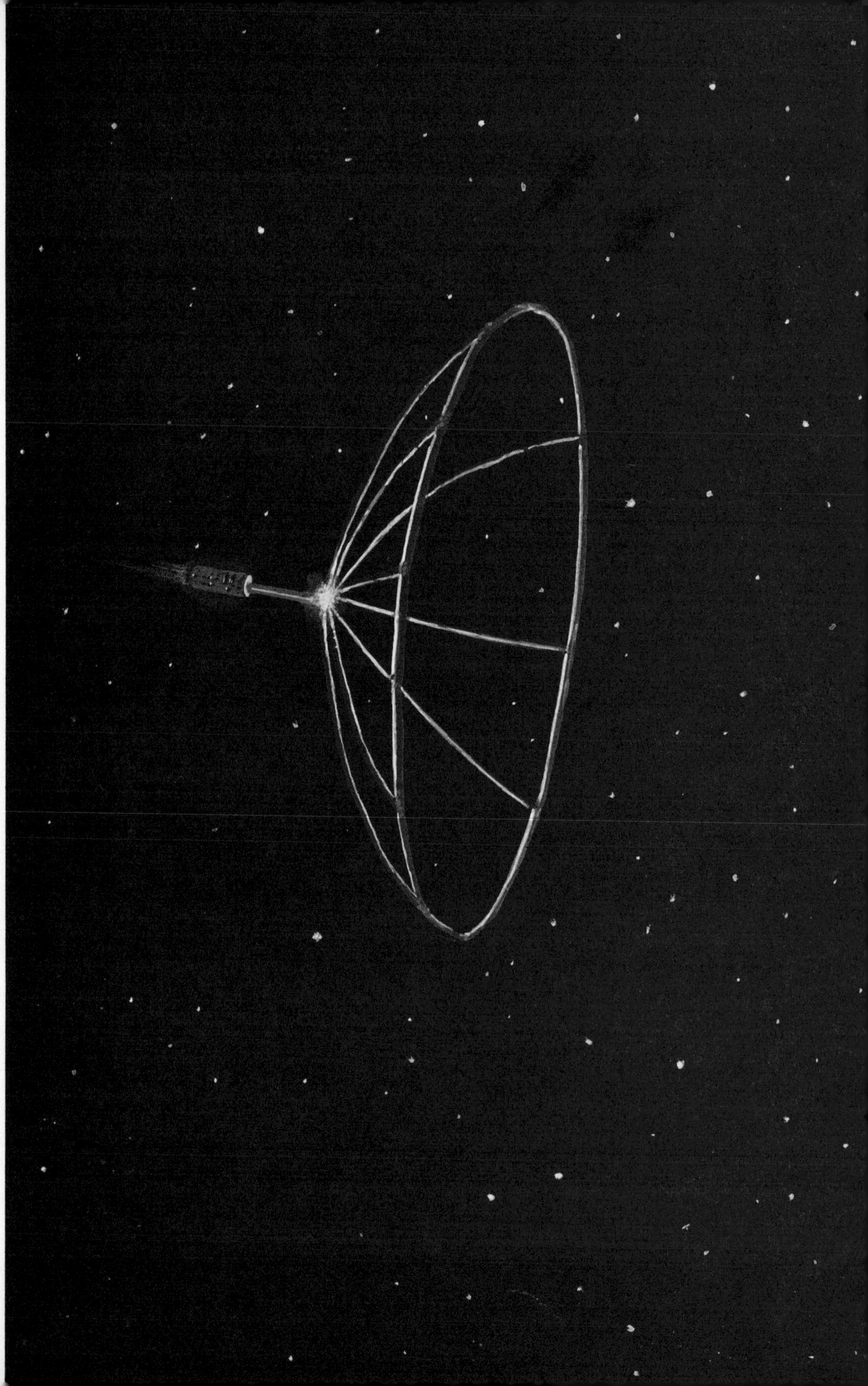

The scoop would not have to be material, since magnetic lines of force could collect hydrogen, particularly where it is ionized (electrically charged) in clouds in which hot type O, B, and A stars are immersed. Assuming the ship could reach 2 percent of light speed (3,600 miles per second), with propulsion supplied by lasers or booster rockets, the scoop would be 40,000 miles across.

Ships with EM scoops of the sizes described above would, with fusion engines, accelerate constantly at 1 g, giving us the capability of galactic voyages. Engines more powerful than fusion engines, capable of converting a larger proportion of mass into energy, would need less hydrogen to achieve 1 g acceleration, and could have smaller scoops. An engine powered by a Black Hole would convert 500 times as much mass to energy as a fusion engine. A Black Hole ship with an 1,800-mile-diameter scoop would be as powerful as a fusion ship with a 40,000-mile-diameter scoop.

Now it is time to return to Black Holes.

A ramjet using matter between the stars offers the ultimate in galactic exploration. Such vessels may even take us from one galaxy to another, where they are connected by a spiral arm. (See the photograph on page 43.)

# 14: Black Holes

Large Black Holes, created by stars, would be places to stay away from. A vessel, once drawn within the envelope surrounding the star, would never be seen again, since even the fastest possible speed, light speed, is less than the velocity of escape from such an object. The ship would be drawn to the core of the Black Hole and reduced, along with everything in it, to the rawest particles of matter.

Before that, however, some interesting things would happen. In the first place, the intense gravity of the Black Hole has the same effect on time as high speeds. As we entered the sphere of the Black Hole, our clocks would go much slower than clocks outside. As we looked back from our ship, we would see the entire future history of the universe, learning the answer to whether it will keep expanding or finally collapse. Unfortunately, we will not be able to pass on this information to anyone.

Once inside the Black Hole, clocks outside would start going backwards in relation to us, at first very quickly, then more slowly as we approached the center. Time outside would be going back-



The mystery of mysteries—
a probe guided by its mother ship
enters a Black Hole. It will never return.

wards and now, looking back, we would see the past, to the beginning of the universe, again obtaining an answer that we would be unable to pass on to the universe outside.

Black Holes can be any size from smaller than a grain of sand to the entire universe. Indeed our universe, if it contains sufficient matter to halt expansion, is a Black Hole. The bigger the Black Hole, the longer the time we could spend in it before being crushed to extinction. A star with twice the mass of our sun would collapse into a Black Hole with a diameter of about 7 miles. In a Black Hole of that size, we would last only 20 millionths of a second. A Black Hole with the mass of a billion suns would give us three hours, and one with the mass of our galaxy, about two weeks. A SuperWorld with sufficient energy at its disposal could create such a Black Hole by carefully maneuvering all the stars of its galaxy into a volume of space with a radius of 2,000 AUs, 50 times the radius of Pluto's orbit.

Rotating Black Holes (and it would seem that most are rotating) would provide even more interesting adventures. A large rotating Black Hole would create a region, called the ergosphere, outside of the dangerous envelope from which nothing can escape. According to the British mathematician John G. Taylor, a ship in the ergosphere would move forward in time in the same fashion as one going at near light velocity. The closer it got to the ergosphere surface, the further forward in time it would go. Then, providing the ship had enough power, it would be able to return to normal space.

It might even be possible, Taylor thinks, to survive entering a rotating Black Hole. The dangerous place in such a Black Hole, he believes, would be a ring around the equator. A ship that entered the Hole north or south of the ring would be able to travel either forward or backward in time: forward as it moved in the direction of the Hole's spin, backward if it were to go in the opposite direction. If it did get out of the Hole, the ship could not return to the universe it had left. It would find itself in a different universe. Such Black Hole voyages to other universes may be the ultimate journeys of mankind.

It is also possible that Black Holes tie different parts of this universe together. The matter that disappears inside the Hole may reappear, flooding out of a White Hole somewhere and somewhen else. If this is true, then Black Holes would be gateways to portions of the universe that are distant in space and time. The Black Hole at Cygnus X-1, for example, might connect to a White Hole in one of the galaxies in the Coma Berenices cluster 70 megaparsecs away and 12 galactic years in the past. In fact, all of space may be essentially a seething mass of tiny Black Holes touching points, which, to our perceptions, are remote in space and time.

In discussing ways in which we might be able to travel between the stars in the future we are, of course, describing ways in which the people of SuperWorlds might be traveling right now. If they have interstellar ramjets scooping hydrogen out of space, we might be able to detect one, a tiny source of EM radiation moving at near light speed. If SuperWorld ships venture into Black Holes, or are wary of them as hazards to navigation, they may leave radio beacons beside them that we might find as we search the skies.

# 15: The World, the Flesh, and the Devil

In exploring the universe for SuperWorlds we have explored our own past and future. We have seen stars being born as our sun was born some 25 galactic years ago, and stars cold and dead as our sun will be 25 or so galactic years from now. And just as, at any instant, among the multitude of stars in our Milky Way galaxy we can find suns in every stage of existence, we know that out there live worlds like ours in every stage of history, from the primitive past of seething seas to the unimaginable future.

There may be planets that have destroyed themselves with plutonium in fits of madness, some where termitelike creatures reign in the dust of cities, others ruled by silent computers whose fleshly creators exist only as data stored in memory banks. And others, perhaps, where beings not too different from man write symphonies for dancing stars.

Aware of these strange possibilities, astronomers watch the heavens with a new kind of fascination. In 1967, when regular pulsating signals were detected from an object designated CTA 102, the mysterious phenomenon was labeled LGM for Little Green Men until someone made the calculations to show they were emitted not by some SuperWorld transmitter, but by a tiny neutron star spinning at many times a second, the shrunken ash of a giant star compressed into matter so dense that a teaspoonful would weigh millions of tons.

They have looked for dim red objects about 1 AU in diameter, giant spheres of matter creating enormous living spaces around their stars. Such objects have been found, but there is no way to tell as yet whether they are indeed artificial, or merely stars in their swollen red-giant phase.

Meanwhile, radio telescopes patiently scan the sky for coded messages, listening for signals inviting young technologies like ours to join some galactic federation, for storm warnings broadcast to a distant space fleet, for the antics of some celestial comic 100 parsecs away. And our little Mariner, Pioneer, and Soviet Mars and Venus probes slowly sail to the planets, sending us close-up pictures of their surfaces.

Next week, next year, in some remote laboratory where tape is being processed, a pattern will emerge—a series of numbers repeated, varied slightly, repeated; or there will be on the surface of Umbriel, a moon of Uranus, a shining metallic disc with strange markings and a tower that looks very much like a radio antenna.

The future that awaits us is not comforting, but we cannot avoid it. It is a rule of existence to be thrust into unknown environments, to be tested according to rules but dimly understood. Each individual experiences this when he first blinks unseeing eyes, emerging, squalling from the dark nurture of the womb. He experiences this at every stage of life, leaving first the nursery, then childhood, then the time of preparation, then parenthood, then the job, then life itself.

Ever searching for security we seek possessions and allies, construct fences and deadly missiles. But in the depths of our being we know that absolute security is unobtainable. As we anchor ourselves behind walls, we fix ourselves as targets for some new menace.

Another way of using the sun's energy. The pressure of its light can move a sail just as the pressure of wind moves a sail on Earth. With thin sails, square miles in extent, a ship sails past Titan. Unlike our Moon, this satellite of Saturn has an atmosphere.

Since the first dark chains of purines, sugars, and acids stumbled into configurations that could make copies of themselves, the inexorable rule of evolution has been: grow and change, or perish. In change there is danger, but a chance of survival. The fossil record bears testimony of millions of creatures that once found a safe corner of this planet and flourished for some millions of years, now known only as indentations in shale or in the lineaments of some strange relation that clambered into colder water.

Mankind has been disrupting the biology of the planet and the appearance of its surface for thousands of years. It is likely, for example, that the ancestors of the American Indian wiped out a number of species of large mammals native to our continent, including the mammoth, the ground sloths, and the dire wolf. Goats bred for human food and clothing have turned large parts of the Middle East and North Africa into desert. Now, as we reach the limits of Earth's resources and see its waters poisoned, hills defaced, and the air becoming unbreathable, we hunger for the unspoiled beauty of a simpler past.

But we cannot return to that unspoiled beauty, which never existed anyway. There were snakes in the Garden of Eden, infections that maimed eyes, brains, and legs, when they didn't destroy, and interior worms that made strong men weak.

In 1929, John Desmond Bernal, the young master of Birkbeck College, University of London, took a long look into the future. It was a difficult time, a few years after a senseless war had destroyed almost an entire generation of European men. Bernal predicted that mankind, in order to survive, would have to overcome three enemies of his reason. He called these enemies, the World, the Flesh, and the Devil.

By the World, he meant the environment, the limits of the Earth's resources.

The Flesh is the limits of the body's physiology—the way tissues succumb to old age and disease, clouding the brain.

The Devil is our psychological instability, appetites and emotions inherited from apes, reptiles, fish, and even more primitive ancestors, that sway us with unreasoning fears and crazy desires.

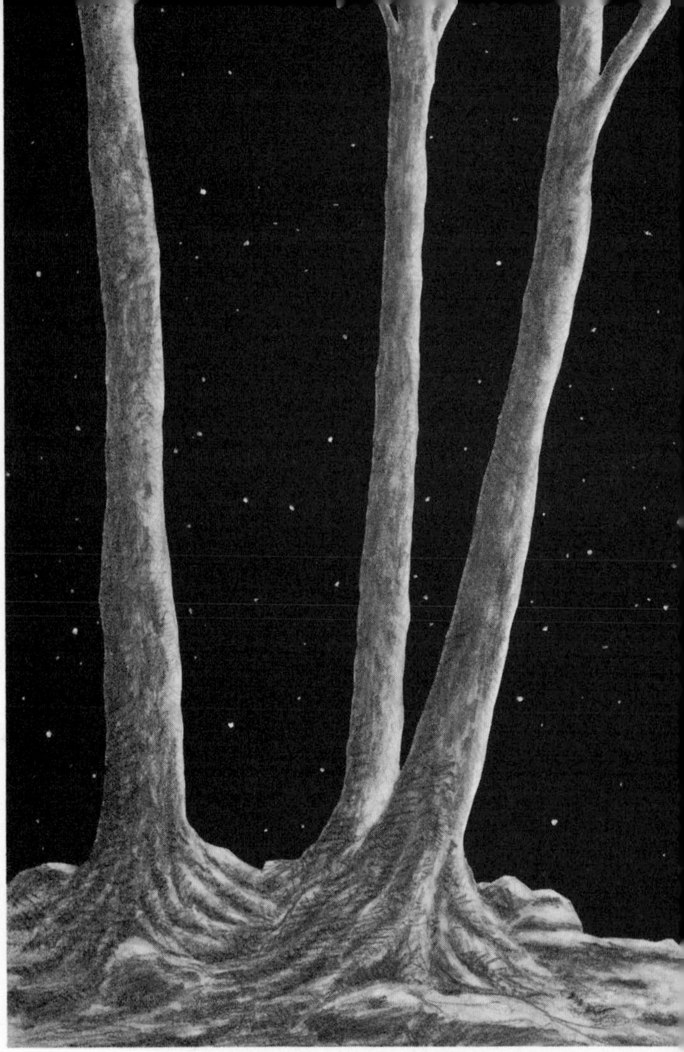

With biological engineering we may design trees that will grow in space, nourishing themselves in the snow and ammonia of comets. Making food and air out of the constant sunlight, these giant plants will provide the necessities of life for human beings living among their roots and lower branches.

Bernal thought that all these enemies could be overcome: the World, by leaving Earth and using the resources of the universe; the Flesh, by blending the body with artificial organs and machines that would nourish and protect the brain; the Devil, by strictly enforced behavior control and control over emotions by drugs or other means yet to be discovered.

Of the three enemies, the Devil appears the most difficult to manage. Behavior control is abhorrent to those who cherish individual freedom. But the Devil is less of a menace when the World is being managed. It was expansion into the New World that nourished freedom in Europe after the sixteenth century. Expansion

into space may make the future of mankind on Earth, as elsewhere, tolerable.

We will be living on other worlds with strange storms and stranger animals, on artificial worlds of our own devising, perhaps on comets in the shade of enormous trees.

Adapting to other conditions, we will become smaller, lighter, heavier, or thinner. Our proportions will change, and with them our idea of beauty and grace. The changes may even be stranger than that, as we master the secrets of the genetic code. We may, as Bernal envisioned, become part machine to defeat the Flesh, or we may grow blood that keeps the arteries young and hearts that remain

Our entire universe may be a tiny particle in some other universe, as each electron in our world may hold a universe of its own. Universes within universes—there may be no end.

renewable. One day there may be men that fly like bees, swim like fish, or crawl under mountains.

Against the unknown, mankind has proceeded with the slender supports of courage and faith. It doesn't matter that faiths have died, to be replaced with other faiths. Faith and its objects, ideas of God and Man, can no more remain fixed than any other principles of life.

The universe, or at least the galaxy, is winding down. Energy moves into ever less usable forms. Freed from the heart of hydrogen, energy radiates to the farthest reaches of space, too weak and widespread to ever again warm a leaf. Helium, the ash of hydrogen, yields energy more reluctantly than hydrogen. As heavy elements come into being there is always some energy missing that will not be recovered.

If life is the destiny of matter, it has an important role in the scheme of things. Life is the one process known that reverses the winding down. It builds complexity out of simplicity, order out of chaos. Consider the leaf, repeating a 100-million-year-old pattern out of sunlight, air, and water. Consider a man, maintaining figure and memory as each atom in his body changes. Consider mankind, a billion-word "book" that has lasted 2 million Earth years. We, and all living things, are forms, not matter—dreams holding molecules in patterns.

We may have been born in these spiral arms to a galaxy that needs us against winding down and Black Holes eating the hearts of stars, perhaps consuming our galaxy from within.

If we have no clearer answers than our ancestors on the African plains, two million Earth years ago, answers to questions of our origins and destiny—our questions move in a bigger space.

There may never be an end to our questions. The universe, as J. Robert Oppenheimer suggested in his last years, may be qualitatively infinite. Its structure and behavior may hold endless surprises. Each of the tiny particles of which we are composed may itself be an entire universe of galaxies. Our great ancient universe may be no more than an electron in some other space.

# Bibliography


General:

*Communication With Extraterrestrial Intelligence,* C. Sagan, ed., MIT Press, 1973.

*Intelligent Life in the Universe,* I. S. Shklovskii and C. Sagan, Dell, 1966.

*Man and His Universe,* Z. Kopal, Morrow, 1972.

*Norton's Star Atlas,* A. P. Norton and J. G. Inglis, 15th edition, Sky Publishing Company, 1966.

*Van Nostrand's Scientific Encyclopedia,* 4th edition, Van Nostrand, 1968.

Chapter 1:

*Final Report of the Scientific Study of Unidentified Flying Objects Conducted by the University of Colorado Under Contract to the United States Air Force,* Dr. Edward U. Condon, Scientific Director, Bantam Books, 1969.

"Space Probe From Epsilon Boötes," D. A. Lunan, *Spaceflight,* 122–137, 1972.

Chapter 2:

"Communications From Superior Galactic Communities," R. N. Bracewell, *Nature,* 186, 670–671, 1960.

Personal communication from D. A. Lunan.

*Proceedings of the Royal Society of Edinburgh,* 50, C. Störmer, part II, No. 15, 1933.

"Space Probe From Epsilon Boötes," D. A. Lunan, *Spaceflight,* 122–137, 1972.

Chapter 5:

"Anti-Matter, Quasi-Stellar Objects, and the Evolution of Galaxies," H. Alfvén and A. Elvius, *Science,* 164, 911–917, 1969.

Chapter 6:

"Planetary Systems Associated With Main Sequence Stars," H. Brown, *Science,* 145, 1177–1181, 1964.

Chapter 8:
*Planets for Man,* S. H. Dole and I. Asimov, Random House, 1964.

Chapter 9:
*This View of Life,* G. G. Simpson, Chapter 13; Harcourt, 1964.

Chapter 10:
"Search for Artificial Stellar Sources of Infra-Red Radiation," F. J. Dyson, *Science,* 131, 1667, 1960.
*Islands in Space,* D. M. Cole and D. W. Cox, Chilton, 1964.

Chapter 11:
*Technical Report TR-17,* Terry Winograd. MIT Artificial Intelligence Laboratory, MIT February, 1971.

Chapter 12:
"How Can We Detect Radio Transmissions From Distant Planetary Systems," F. D. Drake, *Sky and Telescope,* Jan. 1960, 140–143.
Personal communication from D. A. Lunan.

Chapter 13:
"Relativistic Flight With a Constant Thrust Rocket," G. M. Anderson, D. T. Greenwood, *Astronautica Acta,* 16, 153–158 (1971).
"Some Optical and Kinemetical Effects in Interstellar Astronautics," I. E. Sanger, *Journal of the British Interplanetary Society,* 18, 273–276, 1961–62.
"Galactic Matter and Interstellar Flight," R. W. Bussard, *Astronautica Acta,* 6, 181–194, 1965.
"The General Limits of Space Travel," S. von Hoerner, *Science,* 137, 18–23, 1962.
"Problems of Interstellar Propulsion," A. Bond, *Journal of the British Interplanetary Society,* 245–251, 1972.

Chapter 14:
"Black Holes and Gravitational Theory," R. Penrose, *Nature,* 236, 377–380, 1972.
*Black Holes, the End of the Universe,* J. G. Taylor, Random House, 1974.

# Index

Note: Italicized numbers refer to illustrations.

# Map of the Northern Sky
## Showing SuperWorld Locations and Other Points of Interest

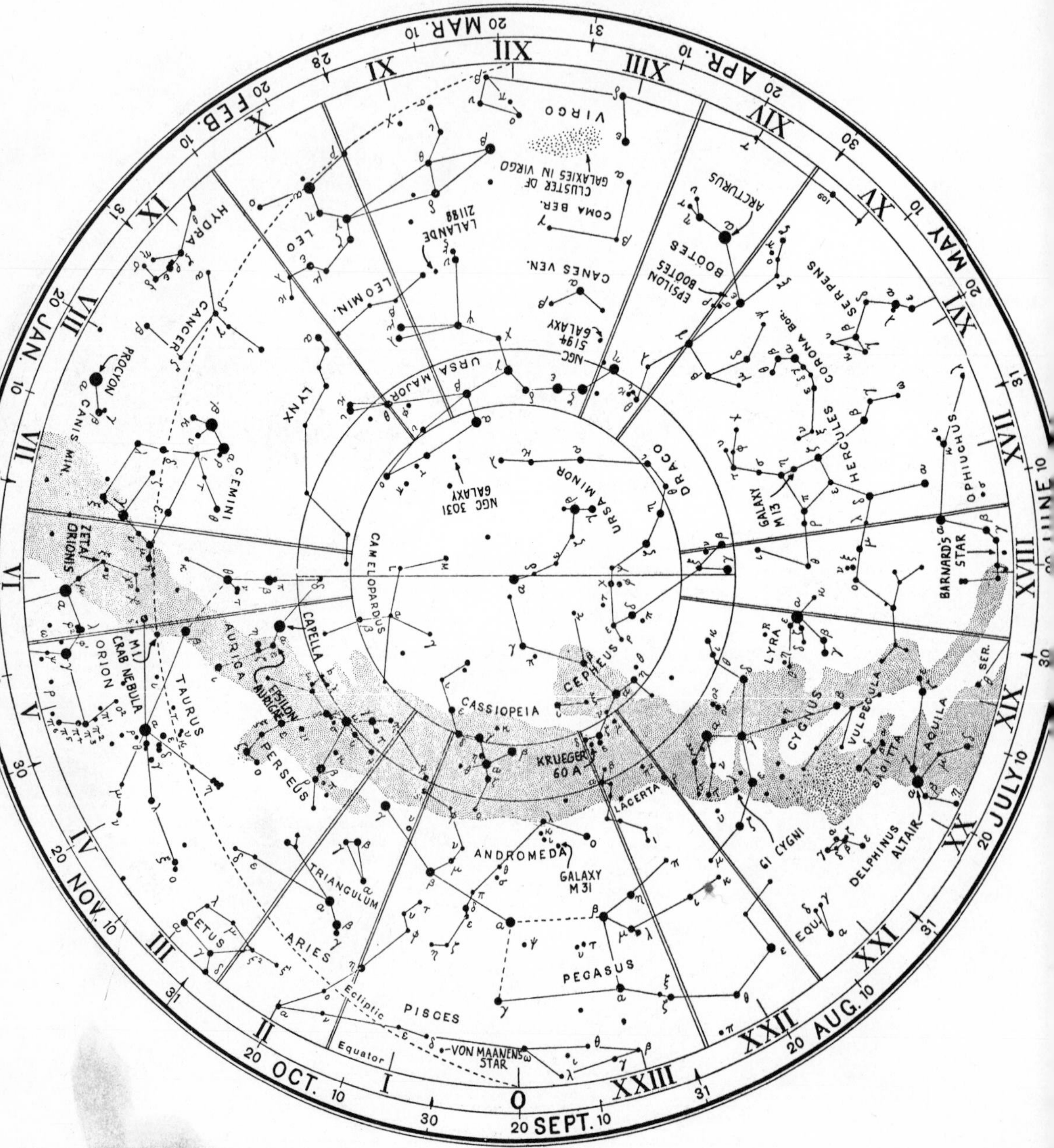


EPOCH 1950

# Map of the Southern Sky
## Showing SuperWorld Locations and Other Points of Interest

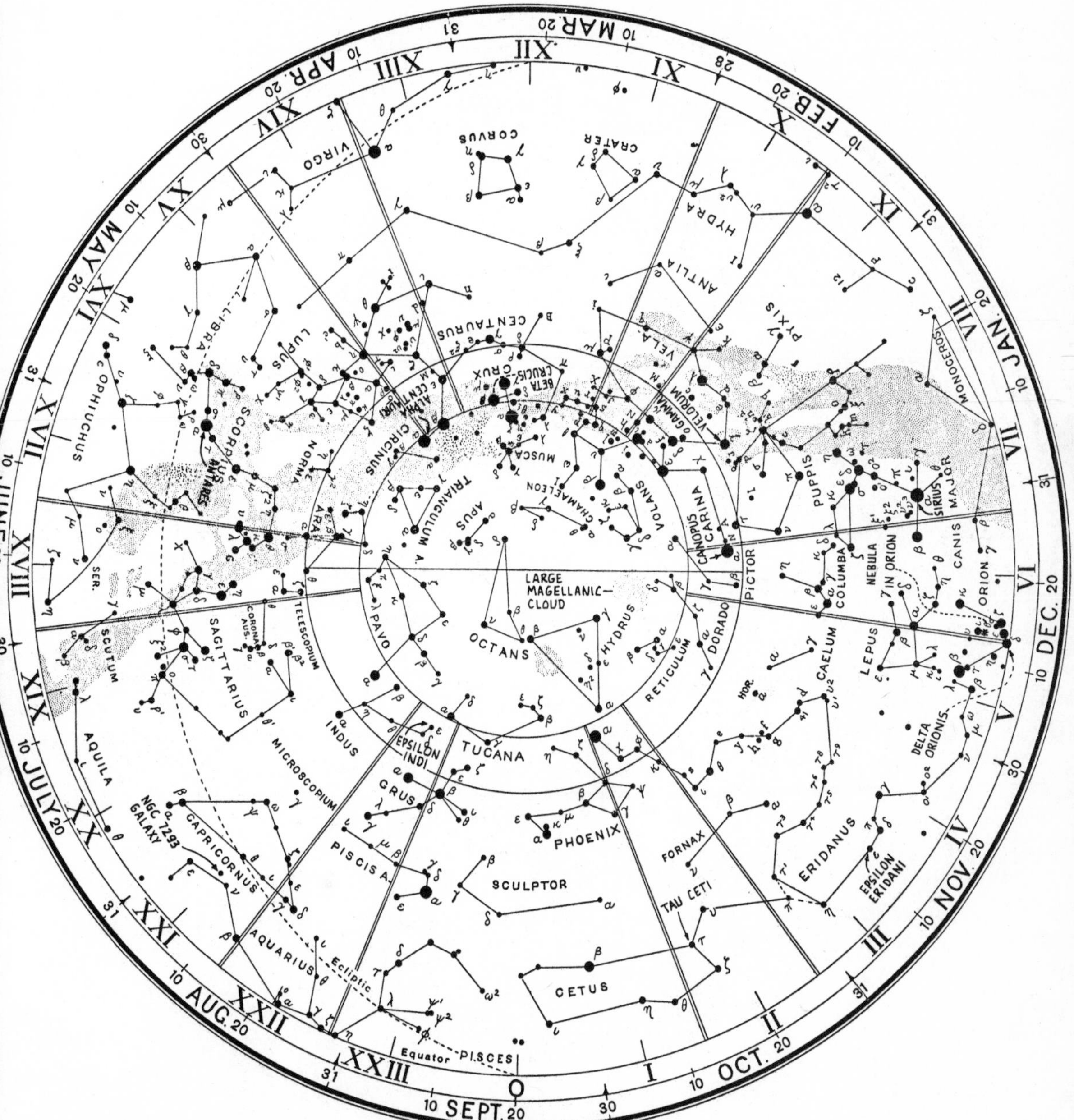


EPOCH 1950